COUNTRY TALES

OLD VETS

Valerie Porter

DAVID & CHARLES

Cover photographs from Rural History Centre, University of Reading
Line illustrations by John Paley

The material in this book was originally published in a fuller form under the title *Tales of the Old Country Vets* (David & Charles, 1995)

A DAVID & CHARLES BOOK

First published in the UK in 1997

A catalogue record for this book is available from the British Library.

ISBN 0 7153 0681 2

Typeset by ABM Typographics, Hull
and printed in the UK by Mackays of Chatham plc
for David & Charles
Brunel House Newton Abbot Devon

CONTENTS

Introduction

One of the great joys of life is listening to stories about personal experiences, and the veterinary surgeons in this book have been most generous with their tales and with their hospitality: it has been a delight to listen to them all. These story-tellers are of an earlier generation who looked upon their work as a way of life rather than a job and were prepared to put up with ridiculously long hours of extremely hard work for a financial reward that was at best adequate but on average far from it. Their strong sense of vocation and dedication surprises even themselves when they look back over their lives.

The country vets bore close witness to immense changes in rural life, especially after World War II. They saw the disappearance of the small family farm and the rush into intensive farming and the housing of animals in large herds or flocks. They witnessed the substantial reduction in dairy cattle and the disappearance of many traditional livestock breeds. They watched the ups and downs of horses, from the high numbers of working horses of old to the new rapid rise in population of 'leisure' horses. They have also ridden on the crest of a wave of 'small animal' work – cats, dogs and other pets, which formed little or no part of veterinary practice in pre-war years.

Some of the stories look back beyond the qualified veterinary surgeon to the old 'veterinary practitioner' who had practised for many years but had not necessarily been through college. Before the practitioner came the cattle doctors and farriers, the latter being essentially shoers of horses but who all had their own secret remedies for every imaginable ailment of the horse, usually passed from father to son for many generations. Some of their treatments were barbaric and probably mutilated or killed more animals than they saved, but some were based on a close familiarity with the horse and its problems, combined with a long tradition of using herbs – the country remedies that were available for the sick, be they livestock or humans. Today veterinary surgeons turn to the big pharmaceutical companies for remedies, rather than to the fields, hedgerows and kitchen gardens.

The publication of James Herriot's first book, *If Only They Could Talk*, in 1970, has been mentioned spontaneously by each and every one of the story-tellers as a turning point in the public perception of their profession. His good-humoured anecdotes about the experiences of a newly qualified veterinary surgeon in the Yorkshire Dales in 1937 unwittingly opened the floodgates: veterinary colleges were deluged by school-leavers eager to become vets. This demand for places threatened to overwhelm the colleges and they opted to set a high standard of A-levels as the main criterion for acceptance. That has led to a different type of person entering the profession in recent years. The emphasis now is often more on technical expertise than a natural empathy with the animals. Many of the older generation of veterinary surgeons would never have been accepted by today's colleges because they would not have had the academic qualifications either to enter it in the first place or to keep up with all the technological innovations.

Those technical advances have been considerable in the last fifty years or so. Highly effective proprietary drugs have replaced the old-fashioned mix-your-own powders and potions which sometimes relied more on good faith than on physical efficacy. Anaesthetics have improved out of all recognition in that period, and there is a powerful range of equipment for diagnosis and treatment, from X-rays to endoscopes. Most of the story-tellers in this book can remember the old pharmacopoeia and the very basic instruments of their trade only too well, and they describe them graphically.

Their stories gradually reveal how the veterinary 'way of life' has changed within living memory, but another theme runs through them all: that, however hard and dirty and frustrating and draining the work might have been, they loved it and would happily go through it all over again. They met a wide range of characters, human and animal; they were out and about and knew every remote corner of the countryside; they were very much a part of the rural community and formed a vital link in its social fabric, particularly in helping farmers to feel less isolated and being a useful channel for the spread of local news and gossip.

Many of them had a lifelong sense of the *fun* of it all. They thoroughly enjoyed themselves, even when up to their knees in mud and manure or up to their armpits inside a labouring cow. Perhaps a good sense of humour is one of the major qualifications needed for being a good country vet – that and a passionate interest in the living creatures who depend on them so much.

NATURE WILL PUT IT RIGHT

ooooo

The small New Forest village attracts summer tourists but it is easy to find peace in its surroundings. Drifting down a long, shady lane, you might notice a field-gate, with a small gate beside it for people to enter the premises – an arrangement that suggests a place where domestic animals range freely. Pausing to look over the gates, you will see an idyllic smallholding: Forest ponies suckling their foals, ducks and chickens gossiping with the geese in the paddocks and orchards, a lop-eared goat minding her own business as she browses along the hedge, and an assortment of dogs lazing about the place, keeping an eye on the livestock. There is an unpretentious country garden, with doves pecking about on the gravel of the drive and perching on a belichened sundial. The general atmosphere is one of informality and relaxation and with a sense of security among the animals and birds. This is very much their home.

The house is of the kind that might once have been a Victorian rectory and it fits comfortably into its garden. A large, benevolent porch shelters trays of hens' eggs and a wicker basketful of ducks' eggs.

There is much cheerful barking to welcome visitors as Lola Breeze opens the sun-faded door. She is as friendly and unpretentious as her surroundings: a small woman, grey hair pulled back tidily in a workaday pony-tail from her well boned, straight-sided face, eyes kindly and ready to laugh but the chin firm enough to suggest the considerable determination that has seen her through a career as a vet since the days when very few in her profession were women. The assorted dogs surge around her in an easy-going way – Lola collects dogs, most of them those that nobody else wanted.

The main reception rooms are living-rooms in the truest sense: one is occupied by Chippy, a grey parrot, and an assortment of budgerigars in a large aviary. In another there is a piano, with sheet music scattered about, and recorded classical music swells from the background to compete with the music of the birds and the dogs. An open fire and the natural warmth of a compassionate woman cheer up a grey, damp morning.

Lola's parents lived in the small rural village of Kingston, just below the South Downs some six miles from Brighton, and she continued to live in the village until she was in her sixties. At home the child was always surrounded by animals – dogs and cats, a pony in a home-made shed, rabbits, guineapigs and hens. They were her natural companions and she finds it hard to imagine any childhood without animals. She knew from the age of seven that she wanted to be a vet and she never changed her mind about that. A vet in due course she became; and a vet she remained, until retiring a dozen years ago at the age of sixty-three.

The Downs were beautiful in those pre-war childhood years; they were carpeted with cowslips and alive with hundreds of summer butterflies. 'My brother and I would wander for miles on the Downs. Or along to the village pond, which was a wonderful place to be – giant newts, water beetles, all sorts of things. We learned such a lot there, especially to be patient, waiting in the shallows for things to emerge from the deep. There were minnows, sticklebacks down in the brooks and there always seemed to be somebody around who would tell us about these things. There was one wonderful old boy who always had time for children: he kept all sorts in jars around his room and he'd tell us everything about the things he found.'

Lola's mother was a concert singer and teacher; her father 'sang in heavy opera, but not for his living' (he was an engineer). Her Cockney grandfather practised herbal medicine in Stratford and this medical link went back several generations on one side of the family; on the other side, a few generations back in Ticehurst, it was farming. Veterinary work manages to link the two.

She went straight from school into the veterinary college, which was based in London's Camden Town but was evacuated to Reading University during the war. There were only about ten women vets in the whole country at the time, and only four or five on her course. She soon began to realise that many potential vets actually knew very little about animals – the spirit of animals, if you like. They were good at anatomy and physiology, perhaps, and at pharmacology and surgery, but they simply knew nothing about handling animals, relating to animals, because even then many of them had never been in the company of animals during childhood.

'The very first exam we had was in animal management. The practical side was a doddle for me – it was basic things like picking up a dog! But the brightest chap, in theory, had no idea. We were all waiting in the college grounds to take our turn when he shot out in a panic, saying, "What *do* I do with *this*? What do I do with this?" He had a bridle in his hand and it was all sort of upside down and he hadn't a clue how to put it all together again. He'd never even seen such a thing before and he certainly couldn't lead or catch a horse, or pick up a dog.

That was in contrast to some of the old school of vets. 'There was an old practitioner ... a practitioner is someone who had been doing the job but didn't have the formal qualifications.

He'd never been to college but he was licensed to practise. He had tremendous experience, this old boy. He'd been farrier on the horse lines during World War II and, goodness me, what he didn't know about horses ... And he described to me how he shoed a team of oxen when they came through Steyning. They used to use those big red Sussex cattle instead of the big horses for ploughing and pulling carts.'

She graduated in 1947 and wondered what to do, but not for long.

'Before I went to college I had been keen enough to operate on kittens and so on; and I suppose that living in the area for so long people knew us – they began to come, and the practice simply began to grow. So I thought, well, I'll stay with it. I was working in our garden shed, with such equipment as there was in those days, which was very basic indeed. I had a sink, and used a bunsen burner for sterilising everything. Penicillin had recently become available but not much else. For anaesthetics we used a morphine-like substance with an antidote, and volatiles like ether or chloroform, and several jam-jars.

'Being on my own and fresh from college I had to learn a lot as I went along. Luckily there wasn't much operating in those days. Then I saw that the college was using intravenous when it first came in, and barbiturates, and I thought, this is for me, and started using it before anyone else in the district did. But it was difficult to get supplies – the war hadn't long been over.'

Lola quickly learned that a love of animals was not enough: it was also essential to understand people. Her clients ranged from lords to criminals, and, frankly, the people were much more difficult to handle than the animals.

'Putting animals down is always sad and at that time it was often particularly heart-rending because for several years the pets had belonged to a son who had been killed during the war

– a last living link with the son. And I had to be the one to say, sorry, we can't prolong its life any longer. It's no good saying that vets shouldn't get involved. You do, of *course* you do.

'But you can fight for them. A nice man brought in the most gorgeous standard poodle; it was white, and immaculate – not a hair out of place. And he said, "Would you put it down, please." And I cringed and thought to myself, *no*! I can't do this. It was only about two years old. So I said, "What's its trouble?" "Oh," he said, "I'm going abroad and I don't want it to go anywhere else because they won't look after it." Well, I could see his point of view but I was *not* going to put that dog down; I was not! It took me half an hour to talk that chap round but I did and I managed to find it a lovely home – it went on to live for another twelve years. In my view the interests of the animal comes first: to me, the *animal* is my client; the owner comes second.

'Some people just aren't happy unless you give some tablets, whether there is something wrong with the poor animal or not. And this is a difficult one. If you want your own way – which I always did! – you have to use a bit of psychology in handling people.'

The garden shed, with a temporary waiting-room in her mother's front room, saw many an event in those early years.

'Oh, that garden shed! When I think back now, I think, "Yoh!" I remember my first operation there: it was a Bedlington terrier needing a caesarean and I was terrified because it belonged to a local surgeon. Fortunately it was a success and he remained as one of my clients for about thirty years. Apart from that, to start with it was mainly routine – checking animals over, dealing with ears and skin problems and anal glands: typical vet's bread-and-butter cases. And it was mainly small animals. I did do horses and big animals for a while but then I realised I couldn't do it all and I needed to specialise. With large animal work, so often economics came into it: you wanted to cure something but you couldn't because it would cost too much for the farmer.

'The practice grew and grew, so I moved out of the garden shed into a small front parlour in a terraced house in the poorer part of Brighton. Mrs Jones's front parlour. She was a lovely lady; she wore a long black skirt and was forever polishing the black range in the tiny kitchen, and making cups of cocoa so strong that it really hit you in the stomach. She was very down to earth. Her father, a farmer, had vaccinated his six children against smallpox himself by scraping their arms and shoving some septic cow pox into them. Well, it did save them all from smallpox.

'Mrs Jones set herself up to protect me from what she decided were "undesirable" clients. When someone came to the door she'd try to get there before I did and would look them over. One day a woman went away again before I had a chance to talk to her: I saw her trolling down the street and I asked Mrs Jones who she was. "You don't want anything to do with the likes of *her* – she's a tart!" she told me firmly.

'I soon outgrew the front parlour, too, and graduated to a shop premises. That was when the real work began. Within a couple of years I was working an eighteen-hour day, with night calls on top of that. Evening surgeries meant coping with an average of about a hundred patients. I reached a stage when I was getting so tired that I couldn't think, and was afraid of making mistakes – it was silly. So I took the plunge and moved the surgery out to my parents' village again at Kingston, dropping about a third of my clients. That took some of the pressure off for a while, though it soon began to build up again. I stayed in Kingston for the rest of my working life, with various branch surgeries as well. It was good fun and it was a challenge, which I love.'

Lola retired from practice after two cataract operations,

because she found that having two contact lenses slowed her down just that bit.

'And I thought, no, I must get out. I was getting extremely tired anyway and I learned something from my mother (who was 98 when she died): she wouldn't sing in public from quite early on because she didn't want not to give of her best. I've seen a lot of vets trying to carry on for too long. But the practice was increasing again and I had become so exhausted that I couldn't even keep food down. And I thought, I don't want to get in a partner: I'll just stop. I'd had thirty-seven good years and I didn't want to let it gradually crumble. So I stopped. And I'm not sorry that I did, because it has all changed so much: I'd hate the work now, it has become so commercial, drugs are so expensive and the companies are always trying to push them at you.

'It has changed. Take X-rays, for example. We had to work without X-ray for a long time and, sure, it's very very useful, but there are many times when you can *feel* – you know exactly what has happened and you don't need to X-ray and charge for that. But today they don't know how to work without all these things. There is a Forester not far from here: his cat was run over the other day and he asked me to have a look at it, although he knows I don't practise any more. I didn't want to interfere because I knew he was a client of a local vet, but I had a look and it had a broken femur, so I advised him to take it to his vet. So he did. When I asked him later how the cat was, he said, "Oh, we had to have it put down. The only other possibility was a complicated pinning job which was going to cost £60, which we couldn't afford, and keep it still or in hospital for six weeks, and we couldn't do that."

'And I thought, well, the number of cats I can remember when there were none of these pinnings and nothing to be done except keep the animal still for three weeks, and they sorted themselves out and did extremely well – might have a slight limp but it never worried them. Usually, you see, Nature works, and whatever you have given wrong, Nature will put right, which is just as well. But I couldn't blame the Forester's vet because today all they have been taught is these complicated pinnings and platings and clever things, which is fine if people can afford it but there are alternatives. I don't think it even occurred to them to do anything other than a pinning – that's how they have been trained. And it makes it all rather expensive.

'Some vets even charge for treating wildlife casualties, or refuse to treat them at all. That's terrible. I mean, you've always got an account up there.' She points to the heavens.

'I never charged for wildies, and there were quite a few of them. A chap suddenly turned up just as we were about to operate on something; he arrived at the surgery with a shoebox and said he'd found this creature on the factory floor and was worried that somebody might accidentally squash it. He'd driven ten miles to bring it in but he didn't know what it was. I looked cautiously into the box and there was this rather evil little face: it was a bat. We delayed the op for a while and I proferred it a piece of mincemeat on the end of some forceps, which it took – yum, yum, that was good! I decided to leave it on the surgery windowsill while we got on with the op, and halfway through there was a whirring sound and we had a bat going blip blip blip around the room, giving an excellent flying demonstration of its radar system.

'Then there was the taxi driver, a very nice client, who was coming back from Brighton one night at about half-past eleven when he accidentally knocked over a fox on the road. It was unconscious, so he put it in the back seat of his cab and drove to my place, woke me up and got me out of bed. I said I'd have a look at it, went to the taxi and there was one rather angry fox, now fully awake and looking at me, saying, "Well, what are you going to do with me now?" Good question! We were surrounded by a large poultry farm so I couldn't just let it go free. I leaped into the taxi, grabbed its brush and scruff and checked it over: it appeared to be perfectly all right. It had just had a glancing blow to the head, which had knocked it out for a while. So we drove back to where it had been found and released it, watching it glide over the fields in the moonlight. I don't think it paid its fare or left the driver a tip, and it probably bored its grandchildren silly with tales of the night it took a ride in a taxi!

'I saw quite a few foxes in the surgery because people in Brighton seemed to think it was fun to have a cub in their flat – until it was about six months old and they'd come and tell me that they couldn't keep it any more. I remember we had two foxes at one time: the dog was very tame, unfortunately – he'd even wag his brush as if he was a dog – but the vixen was not and I never tried to tame her. It's not fair on a wild animal to keep it unless it is quite unable to fend for itself in the wild; and if you make them tame they risk running up to the first person they meet, which might not be a good idea! Anyway, we kept the pair through what was a very harsh winter but I wanted to release them as soon as possible. Fortunately we knew a chap in Friston Forest who agreed that we could bring them over there and that his son would keep an eye on them after release. They took me and the two foxes in a small jeep right into the depths of the forest and we let them go. Well, the vixen was off like a streak – she would be fine. And the dog fox trotted off for a little way but then something frightened him and he came running back to us, which was rather pathetic! The son took him for a walk and had to accompany him for about three quarters of an hour before the fox suddenly began to remember his instincts, looking for water in the back of a tree and so on.

'There was also an unconscious badger brought in by the roadman, bless him. She had obviously been knocked out by a car and we put her in a loosebox. And when she came round and found herself confined, she was very angry indeed! Very powerful animals, badgers, and really quite dangerous: I'd never advise anyone to handle one unless they knew a great deal about badger behaviour.

'People quite often brought in wild birds. I've always kept budgies and canaries anyway, foreign birds, so people knew that we were interested in birds. But they are rather difficult because they go so quickly just from shock and trauma. By the time you get them, somebody has already picked them up and put them unwittingly in a state of shock before you even start to treat them. We've had owls, kestrels and so on – difficult, but we always tried, though we only ever had any success at all with about one in five. We often saw seabirds, of course, gannets and so on, oiled or injured.

'And someone brought in a boa constrictor once which had curled itself around the radiator for the winter and burned itself when the radiator became too hot. I had no idea what to do with it; I'd never dealt with a snake before. But I put on something soothing and not too dangerous, and it did very well.

'Tortoises – mown-off tortoises would come in: people had run over them with the lawnmower. We repaired the shells with Polyfilla and sometimes painted it to match if we had the time. They seemed to do very well.

'I remember an old boy in the village phoned up and said could I go at once because there was a wild animal – he thought it had escaped from the circus and it had attacked him as he went up his garden path, so he didn't dare leave the cottage. I asked him to describe it and he said that, well, it was striped, rather like a cat. So I thought, this was going to be rather jolly!

I armed myself with a large cage and a blanket. I was pretty worried about what I would find when I got there but I marched brazenly up the drive. And rushing down the garden path to meet me came a very pretty little polecat ferret, saying, "Do pick me up! Thank goodness somebody's come!" I was just as relieved to see it as it was to see me, I can tell you! The old boy wouldn't believe it was only a ferret but the whole escapade did my reputation a great deal of good.

'The bulldog episode was even better in that respect. I thought I had finished one day when the phone rang. There was a very excited voice, speaking very fast and out of breath: "Can you come at once – the dog's gone mad – we got it in the bathroom – it's making a *dreadful* noise!" So I asked, "Where are you?" "I'm in the 'phone box!" That's a good start, I thought. I rephrased it: "What's your address?" Eventually I got directions, and gathered that they had bought the dog the night before in the pub and that it had suddenly "gone mad". Well, I was young and foolish enough to think that I could deal with this one on my own, even if I didn't particularly want to. I armed myself with my case and my anaesthetics and my blanket.

'That blanket is the most important piece of my equipment, you know. There are always going to be one or two difficult animals but I usually get round it. The nervous ones, I give them time and talk to them a lot – that's really all they need. Never in thrity-seven years did I use a dog-catcher; I think they are diabolical and make it far worse for a frightened dog. But if an animal is difficult to handle, if you have a dog that you can't pick up and it is snapping and everything, well, if you can cover it with a large blanket, quietly and gently, then pick it up in the blanket and talk to it *through* the blanket – you can usually get round it that way.

'Anyway, so there I was with my blanket facing the prospect of a mad bulldog. And it was indeed making a most extraordinary noise on the other side of the bathroom door. The family sat on the settee downstairs, all semi-hysterical. Well, I felt honour bound to brave it out. I held my case in front of me (hopefully the dog would hit that first), opened the door carefully and saw at the other end of the bathroom one white bulldog. It took off – and just in that split second I realised that the noise she was making was not growling. It clicked in the back of my mind that somewhere in my college notes was the fact that bulldogs can have long soft palates and noisy breathing when they get excited.

'And a second later she had landed in my lap and was licking me to death, saying, "Thank goodness you've come! Really, those people don't know *anything*!" She was a super dog. I stayed in there and talked to her for a while; I filled the basin full of water and let her stand up and have a drink, sploshing it all over the place, and I thought I'd let the family stew for a minute or two. I put the lead on her and by then the chap had come up and called out from a safe distance in a quavery voice: "You all right?" "Yes," I said, "and we're coming out." "Ooh," he squealed, and I heard him retreating rapidly downstairs. Out we came, me with Bluebell on her lead, and found that all three members of the family were hiding behind the settee, just their heads popping out. I explained what the problem was but they wouldn't believe me. They just said, "No, we don't want it, we don't want it – put her down, put her down." I asked weakly if I could find her a home and they just said, "We don't want her, we don't want her – just take her away!"

'So I marched out of the front door and the timing was impeccable: a police car had just arrived, summoned by the family, and two enormous coppers were putting on huge leather gauntlets and arming themselves with dog-catchers, chains and goodness knows what. "Is that the dog?" they said in amazement. "Yes, she's perfectly all right," I said and left them with jaws dropped down to here. Right, I thought, that's one up to me.

'A few days later I was beetling through a not very built-up area at 40mph without concentrating and a police car waved me down. Oh dear, I thought. He started to get stroppy because it was a 30mph limit and he got out his notebook, asking my name. When I told him, he said, "Oh, are you the vet that went to the bulldog the other day? Oh, well, don't speed through here again, will you." It was a triumphant moment for me: it had done my reputation no end of good! And we found Bluebell a very good home as well.

'But it doesn't always work so well. I was asked to go and see a dog at a house – the owner had told me it was nervous and he didn't want to bring it into the surgery. Well, there was this large, nondescript dog running around and seeming quite all right. It lay down and the man told me that it had a bad ear. I went over cautiously, saying, "Hallo, old boy." I saw his lips beginning to go up and I thought, oh yes. I did nothing more, staying still for a moment, and he came at me, grabbed my wrist and tried to detach my hand from my arm. The owner just stood there. I asked him to get a lead but he just wrung his hands and did nothing. I had to use my free hand to prise the dog's mouth open – he was pulling me down and I knew it would mean trouble if he got me on the ground. Of course he got my other hand but I managed to grab my stethoscope from the table and shove it in his mouth, and he chewed madly on that instead.

'And then I went and bled all over their beautiful grey bathroom, all over the carpet. And I hope they never got the stain out! He told me that he couldn't put a lead on his own dog because it would attack him. Mental dog, and mental owner. Anyway, I could hardly use my hands but I had to drive six miles home and take surgery that evening.

'I've been bitten several times, of course, but never savaged like that and always because it was my own fault for being over-confident or a bit careless. That was the only time that it was not my own fault. Small dogs, especially terriers – they can sometimes be a bit snappy but they are usually all right. And if the owner picks up a small dog and puts it on the surgery table, it seems to feel less than confident to have a go at you: it just waits to see what's going to happen next.

'Of course, you can get bitten by cats, too, and that can be worse than a dog: it's more likely to go septic. One of the funniest characters was Daisy the Basher, a Blue Siamese. She would come into the surgery and be very good: I could take her out of her basket and she would let me do anything to her that needed doing, anything and everything. Then she would go back into her basket of her own accord – and that was the critical moment! If I left my hand on the table, she wouldn't bite or scratch but she would deal me a hammer blow: wallop! The first time she did that, I wasn't expecting it and it really was like being hit with a sledge hammer: my whole hand was bruised right across. It really taught me just how strong a cat's paw can be. It was a matter of, "Right, that's *that* for you!" Then she would calmly climb into her basket and go home. It was always after I had finished, never before or during. We had a very soft spot for Daisy the Basher.'

Lola came to live in the Forest after her retirement from the Kingston practice. The family had often come to the area when she was young and she had always loved it. She wanted to be far enough away from Sussex not to 'embarrass' the 'very nice chap' who had taken over her practice, and she also wanted to be able to ride. She loved her present home on sight; it had enough ground for her ponies and she could ride straight into the Forest.

'We have a love/hate relationship with the foxes here. I feed them every night because it keeps them out of the hen house a bit, but we can't really control them. I had peacocks but the foxes took seven in four days, in broad daylight – we were careful to round them up at night and shut them in, which was always a performance, stupid birds! I do miss them, in spite of their screeching. We had some bantams that learned to roost up in the trees very safely, but the fox used to get them early in the morning when they came down, as soon as it was daylight. Foxes are fascinating animals but I find them less fascinating when they suddenly take one of my special pets. But it is something that they do – and I don't believe all this nonsense that they kill things for "pleasure". They just kill; that's their nature, and then if they are left alone they come back and collect the rest later. You can't blame them. But they are so *clever*: they've beaten us time and time and *time* again! And then there are the squirrels: I watch them going off with a couple of hens' eggs tucked under each arm, raising their hat to me as they go!'

Lola is clearly happy living in the Forest – it is a way of life that seems to suit her very well. It is time to take a look around the smallholding that surrounds her home. Access to the paddocks and orchards is through a neat, clean yard edged with looseboxes, in the first of which a Forest mare is watching over her foal. In another, the chocolate-coloured goat is standing on her hindlegs, forefeet on top of the lower door; a gingery rabbit keeps her company in the straw, and the white doves roost overhead. The goat is Poz, a 'semi-Nubian', her part ancestry betrayed by her long lop ears. She is a most friendly creature, talking in little muttered bleats and alert to everything that goes on in the yard.

'People often look over our field gate and gawp at the ducks and things, which I'm more than happy for them to do. Once I was walking round the yard one day when I noticed a family hanging over the gate and I thought, that's all right. But then they started screaming and running up the lane. What the dickens? I thought.

I stopped them at the gate and asked what the matter was. "Your rottweiler's coming up the field to attack us!" they said. Well, that was rather strange: I didn't have a rottweiler. I made them stay there while I went to have a look. And it was dear old Poz, who loves people: she was coming trotting up to the gate with her ears flapping up and down! It was just a few days after some of the media scare stories about rottweilers. Really, some people know nothing about animals!'

Lola's first goats were, as ever, acquired somewhat by accident. 'They came upon me. A nanny goat with two little kids came into the surgery. The owners of the kids were two little girls with great big blue eyes brimming with tears. They said, "We can't do anything with them. We have got to get rid of them. We've phoned up the goat society and they said to put them in the *freezer*!" So those kids stayed with us instead, and stayed until they were about fourteen years old. It's always a problem for people: what to do with billy kids. It's why I never put Poz in kid. But she does a spontaneous combustion every now and then, so I do have goat's milk from time to time.

'Sometimes goats can be quite impossible to milk. I had one called Tapioca, a big nanny, horned. The first time I tried to milk her, she wasn't having it and I finished up roping her fore and aft. I managed to wring out about half a pint of curious liquid while she was tied up like that. I put the bucket down and, roped or not, she managed to extend her neck like a telescope, saying, "I'll have that!" and drank it. You had to laugh.

'I used to have a couple of Jersey cows in Sussex: I loved them dearly but I didn't have enough time for them. The field was about a quarter of a mile from the house. There was one old Jersey who was so good as her milking time would always be interrupted by other people's animals needing this and that she was so patient with me. I used to milk her out in the field when

I could find a moment and I remember once I was out there milking in the moonlight at half-past twelve at night – I had only just finished work. Suddenly a chap drove up in a dress suit, all very posh, asking the way to somewhere. He looked at me a bit oddly but went off to his party, which happened to be with people I knew. Apparently he told them: "There's a mad woman milking a cow in the field in the middle of the night!"

'Here, I have two Forest ponies which run the Forest. But they come back for food and they come back in bad weather for the night – help-yourself bed-and-breakfast whenever they wish. They are not leadable or anything, though you can handle them. And if I meet them when I'm out in the Forest for a walk, they greet me as if I was another horse. They come with me for a little way and then, well, you know ... And it's very nice, a good feeling. They also come back here for foaling: they turn up two days before the foals are due, check the boxes and make their choice, insisting on the box they want to foal in, and say, "All right, we'll stay *here*." Then off they go when they are ready to do so. I like that.'

She looks around at her New Forest holding, teeming with animals and warmth, swallows swooping above the yard, dogs mooching about the place, the soothingly repetitive sound of the doves, and the afternoon sun breaking through at last. She has let the mare out of the loosebox, and the pony ambles her own way to the paddocks, her foal frisking impishly, still not wholly in control of its own long, strong legs, still full of juvenile optimism and curiosity at the wonders of a world that it does not yet know.

'I haven't talked so much for a long time!' Lola tells me quietly. And I feel privileged to have listened to a woman of such sincerity, a woman who has such a natural affinity and compassion for animals of every kind – including human ones.

From Mules to Montgomery

ooooo

The Welsh borders and Herefordshire: strong, productive, rich, dark green landscape with rounded, kindly hills patchworked with fields; here and there a knobblier, browner hill loftier than the others. Good hunting country, they say – there is very little barbed wire in this region of hedgerows, dotted with fine trees, and there are plenty of livestock too, cattle and sheep.

It is a fine, sunny day, with thin mares' tail clouds sweeping high up into a clear blue sky, combed out by the breeze. Winding roads through the hills, empty roads past old farms, stone cottages, black-and-white cottages, a farmhouse with ancient low brick walls lining its approach.

The road wanders in and out of Wales, uncertain about the border, and its verges are bursting with wildflowers. I reach the old town of Montgomery at the top of a hill, a town so small that it feels as friendly as a village, although it is a county town with a long and venerable history. It has a good, solid town hall at the top of the short, market-square-like Broad Street. They tell me it is famous for two things, at least: its castle, and the robber's grave.

A narrow lane climbs out of the little town, and the peace of the area steals over you as you look out across the vale to those friendly little hills not far away. It is a very welcoming place to be. The veterinary surgeon's nameplate, recognisable by the horse and sheep that decorate it, marks a laneside house surrounded by fields. The house's name, Tagfaen, means 'a lovely place'.

Terry Boundy pours the coffee and sits, albeit restlessly, at the kitchen table. In the centre is an assorted collection of wildflowers in a tumbler of water, among them a soft mauve flower that is hard to identify.

'Salsify!' says Terry. 'I found it on the corner of the lane this morning and looked it up.' He has a passion for wildflowers and knows a great deal about them; his private reference library on the subject is extensive.

He built this house four or five years ago next to his previous home, a bungalow that they named Killaganoon, where he had built his surgery and an impressive range of outbuildings to accommodate animal patients. The surgery is imaginatively lined with non-slip tiles that he first saw around a swimming-pool.

The buildings are now stables, with well groomed ponies at livery peering over the half-doors, but there was a time when the yard would have been choc-a-bloc with sheep. Farmers brought their sheep in for treatment by Terry and there would be a queue of them, much bleating of animals rounded up off the hills, pouring into the yard and surprised to be here, much laughing and chatting, quite a social occasion at the height of the lambing season in particular. In the little surgery three vets would have been working flat out, lambing the ewes, carrying out caesareans when required, dealing with up to a thousand in the season. It had been one of Terry's best ideas: to encourage the sheep to come to the yard, rather than the vets going out to the sheep.

Although there is a gentle lilt to Terry's voice, he was not born a Welshman; the lilt has come gradually after living and working among the Welsh for nearly half a century. His family came originally from Cumberland. He was born in May 1920 and in due course found himself at a grammar school in Liverpool: his father was chief engineer with the Blue Funnel line.

While Terry was still at school in Liverpool, a vet started in practice a mile or two from the house, doing his rounds on a bicycle and always charging half-a-crown, whatever the job – it was mostly docking puppies and castrating tomcats. The schoolboy offered to help out by cleaning the kennels. Terry had a dog at home and was always drawn to dogs and cats, so that it was hardly surprising that, on matriculation in 1936, he announced that he wanted to be a veterinary surgeon. He received good advice from his employer: 'Terry, that's no use unless you go farming first.' So he took a job in Lincolnshire for a year on a small farm, handmilking fifteen cows at five in the morning to get the milk on the stand by seven, at sixpence a gallon.

He entered the University of Liverpool Veterinary School in 1937, a time when, he explains, 'they were begging for vets'. There were only fourteen of them in his first year, including three girls. They found themselves mixing with the medics and dentists and also discovered that they needed to catch up on a lot of basic science: organic chemistry, physics and so on.

'It was wonderful. You learned a lot of anatomy and you learned it properly – you learned to know what was underneath the skin. We dissected the horse; we dissected the dog; we played with bones and handled them over a period of twelve months, so we had a very good knowledge of anatomy.'

During the summer he went to a cheese-making farm beneath the White Horse near Westbury, Wiltshire, where they milked 110 cows by hand, just before the farm changed over to milking machines.

'The interesting thing there was these wonderful Irish labourers. They lived in the barn – there'd be beds for them on the floor and about seven or eight of them lived in the barn. They were great pals of mine; they taught me how to drink beer and smoke a pipe. They'd take me down to the local on Saturday night and carry me home afterwards. But then, you see, we weren't drinking beer down there: it was this raw cider!'

During his second year at Liverpool he was fortunate enough to meet the remarkable lecturer, A.C. (Arnold) Shuttleworth:

'Brilliant man. He'd been injured badly in his head in World War I but he was still brilliant. He was our anatomy teacher in bones and did surgery as well. And he was in the Royal Army Veterinary Corps, Territorial Army: he used to go off riding each weekend. One day he called me over and said, "Would you like to learn to ride a horse?" Well, definitely I'd like to learn. So he said, "Would you go and work in a riding school for a few weeks?" And I did so: I used to get the six o'clock train in the morning from West Derby and I'd be at my destination by about half past six, then walk a mile or so to the stable. It was just cleaning out and basic husbandry, but I *loved* it, loved every minute of it. I'd never had anything to do with horses at all before that.

'I became very friendly with the owner of the riding school, Harold Parker, a real horse-dealer type. One day in 1938 he told me that I ought to be in the yeomanry. I said, "What's the yeomanry?" He said, "It's a horse army, Territorials."'

Terry duly joined the Duke of Lancaster's Own Yeomanry in Liverpool as a farrier:

'I had a most marvellous time in camp in Yorkshire. We had this wonderful squadron drill with chainmail on our shoulders, and bandoliers across our chests; we wore breeches and puttees and we were taught how to use the cavalry thrusting sword. Fantastic fun! And all these horses. I discovered that Parker and a couple of other people used to have horses spread all over the countryside that they would gather together and hire to the yeomanry, going from one yeomanry to another for the camping season. Parker had at least two hundred of these horses for hire.

And he was mixing with an old fellow, a vet called Leach, from Crewe. I think the only drugs Leach used came in two packets, one green and the other red: one was Epsom salts and the other was common salt. He might not have been very good academically but he had a great knowledge of horses.

'In the middle of camp I had to go back and take my second-year examination – and got first class honours. You see, the exam was an oral one and I was wearing my uniform and the examiners only wanted to ask me about the cavalry!

'Towards the end of that camp, Parker and Leach asked me to take 300 horses by train from the Yorkshire camp to Penrith, overnight. We loaded all these horses in the train and I sat in the guard's van at the back. And I remember so well getting off at Penrith very early on Sunday morning, unloading the horses and riding bareback through the empty streets – riding one and leading three others.

'But my father kept on pointing out that there was going to be a war. I wasn't worried – hell, I was already in the army. And in August 1939, of course, we were called up. I went with my unit to Ramsbottom, in Lancashire, where we slept on the floor in the school and we put all the horses in the mills. Most of the horses were provided by Leach and Parker, who were now making a mint of money by selling horses to the army. They were basically hunters, and the little horses that used to be called vanners, the sort of animal that would deliver the milk and the coal. Light horses, small horses, mainly cobs, and coal-cart horses and all sorts, all shapes and sizes, and police horses.

'We farriers set about shoeing all 300 of them. They all came in differently shod, of course – police horses shod so as to stop them slipping about on the cobbles, hunters shod differently from the vanners and so on. So we shod them all with "universal" shoes, army style.

'After about six weeks a message came round: all the horses were being taken away, they were going to a cavalry brigade heading for Egypt. And we were to be turned into light anti-aircraft units. I said to myself, right, that's the end of session one. What do I do now?'

He intended to carry on as a bombardier in the artillery but his father told him that veterinary students who had passed their second examination were 'reserve'. He consulted his farrier major and the Veterinary Officer, who instantly gave him a warrant to go home, that very afternoon. So he went back to college.

For the next three years, Terry served as Sergeant in the University Officer Training Corps while he continued his studies at Liverpool. Leach had already introduced him to Bob Tuckey, who had an extensive cattle practice at Whitchurch in Shropshire. Almost as soon as Terry came out of the army, he began seeing practice with Tuckey every vacation.

'Tuckey was one of the old school. In those days it was accepted that, as a student, I had to work. I washed the car every morning, and every day I polished his boots – three pairs of those brown polo-type boots. I cleaned and boiled all his instruments, and prepared his medicines – things like making up calcium boroglutamate solutions for milk fever injections by filtering the powder through cotton wool into a bottle with hot water.'

Towards the end of his time at Liverpool, the whole pattern of teaching veterinary science was radically changed when a most famous surgeon, Professor J.G. Wright, came up from London and set up the first field station in any British veterinary school.

'He had such a different approach. You could sit and listen to Professor "Jugjug" and you didn't need to write a note: everything he said went in and it stayed in. He was so practical and he revolutionised our approach. He came in September 1941. In July 1942 fourteen of us took our finals and there was only one failure – in complete contrast to former years, when there would have been only one pass!'

Thus having gained his qualifications as a veterinary surgeon in the summer of 1942, Terry joined Tuckey as his assistant. A lot more work seemed to be coming in, especially fertility work, an aspect which Terry himself had introduced into the practice.

'It was very hard work, very hard, in the blackout and all that. I had one half-day off in seven and also had to do most of the work that came in after six in the evening. My pay was £9 a week and my keep. After a couple of months the itch to get back into the army was too strong to resist and anyway Leach was always encouraging me to do so.'

He volunteered for the Royal Army Veterinary Corps and was commissioned late in 1942 as a lieutenant. At that stage of the war there was not much of a demand for army veterinary surgeons, but that all changed in 1943 when the Japanese entered the war and made their way into Singapore, heading for India. Suddenly Terry found himself preparing to head east.

'We had a month in Doncaster and then straight out to India, where they conditioned us in Rawlpindi and the Punjab. Then I went to two remount depots with something like 12,000 horses and mules in each of them, no mechanical transport at all so you had to ride. Oh, it was a wonderful experience! I loved every minute of it. Then I went to Assam, where we had mostly mules.

'Our biggest veterinary problem was surra, like the tsetse fly; it caused trypanosomiasis, or "trip". Each week, throughout the campaign, we had to carry out blood tests and smears for every single equine in the division. Any animals that tested positive were ridden back to Imphal by the mobile veterinary section.

'I was with the 23rd Indian Division for a while, then I was captain-in-charge of the 7th Indian Mobile Veterinary Section. I was in on the movement of the 5th Indian division into Imphal by air when they were completely surrounded by the Japanese in 1943 or 1944. We had to provision them, we moved in all their mules. I think that was the first recorded movement of equines in large numbers by air. We loaded seven mules at a time into Dakotas, divided by bamboos into groups of seven, and their mule leaders went with them.

'We had a number of horses for riding but we were pack transport and these were all mules, entirely different creatures. Little Chinese mules, very tiny, and very few of them were shod as their feet were so hard. We had the big type of American mules as well but most of our animals came from South Africa. We had pack companies and we had the Indian artillery mules, carrying the parts of the broken-up gun. The mules were so useful: we could get into places that mechanical transport couldn't even get close to; we were fighting up in the mountains, remember, and you never knew where you were. Most of the mules had to be devoiced, of course, and we had these centres where groups of veterinary surgeons would devoice them. Otherwise the whole world would have known exactly where we were!

'When I was in the 7th Indian Division in 1943 we went down to Kohima and the Japs came in the back and cut the road below Kohima, completely surrounding the area. The big battles of Kohima and Imphal were the turning point of the war – the *whole* war – where the Japanese were defeated and started to go back.

'I loved it all. I was frightened most of the time, as most of us were. You know, lots of the veterinary officers in the Veterinary Corps did remarkable jobs. A number of them were lost in those campaigns, especially the Chindits group. They were willing to go anywhere and they never turned a hair.' By now it was Major Terry Boundy and he was in the 23rd Indian Division supervising the training and care of all the mules and horses designated for the initial invasion of Malaya at Port Swetenham.

'We trained the mules to swim ashore from landing-craft. And we were all loading up at Bombay, waiting to go, when the atomic bomb was dropped and that was the end of it all.

'It was a remarkable period of my life and, thinking back on it, I wish I had stayed in the army a little longer. It's the travelling, you were *doing* something, you were going into areas with problems, and there was that little element of risk about it all.'

In 1946 Terry was demobbed and decided to marry the girl he had first met in 1942, when she was a decoder in the Wrens. He set about looking for a job but it wasn't easy: 'The basic work was there but there wasn't the *amount* of work. Remember, we only started to use penicillin in veterinary practice in about 1946. Sulphonamides came here in about 1940, I suppose. So in 1946 we were still mostly relying on Epsom salts, chlorodyne, sodium siliciate and "get down on your knees and pray"!'

Eventually he came to the Montgomery practice. 'When we first came here, a new assistant doctor came into the town at the same time. When a local bigwig heard that a new doctor *and* a vet were coming in, he declared that houses must be found for both of us, and houses were found. We were put into Crogbren, in May 1947. It was one of those squatters' cottages built years and years ago around a chimney. You know the sort of thing: if they had put the chimney in and built a house round it and had smoke coming out of the chimney by nightfall, they could stay. It was a small cottage; I've still got the marks on my head from banging into the beams! There wasn't even a loo except for one of those dry-powder things.'

At first there seemed to be no work at all for the new veterinary surgeon: 'My wife and I were two English intruders into this area and there were Welsh veterinary surgeons in neighbouring practices. There was just no work coming in and I'd often do a forty-, fifty- or even sixty-mile round trip to see just one or two animals. The paying was a bit difficult: farmers usually paid you only once a year, after the October sales.

'The very first time I was in Welshpool market, soon after I came here, a horse breeder came up to me. "I gather you started a practice at Montgomery?" he said. "Do you know anything about horses?" I told him I'd spent four years in the army with them. "Oh," he says, "you'll do. Have you ever castrated a horse?" I said yes, plenty of them – I'd had a lot of castrations with Tuckey in Cheshire, you see. "Right," he said, "tomorrow morning." So I went along about nine o'clock in the morning and he was in the yard. "Where's the horse?" I asked. "Ah," he said, "come on, we're going to have something to drink." Oh oh, I thought. Two White Shield Worthingtons. Well, they are pretty potent. And a couple of cigarettes. "Come on," I said, "let's get this job done." So we went out to the stables and there was an eleven-year-old Shire stallion! "Where's the helper?" I said. "Me and thee," he replied. I was supposed to do a standing castration with just him to hang on to the beast. "Oh, get on underneath, laddie," he said, "you know your job – you can do it."

'We only ever had local anaesthetics then. What we used to do was put a twitch on, get underneath, catch hold of the testicle, shove about 10cc of local into it on either side, smoke a cigarette and by the time you'd finished you could get under there and castrate it. So that's what I did, and that damn great stallion never moved! We'd finished the job in half an hour. "Come on," he said, "we'll go back in the house and have another drink." Another couple of White Shields!

'Horse work is all that I'd wanted to do when I came out of the army. I'd had extensive cattle experience in the Whitchurch practice, so I knew what I was talking about with cows and that went down well. But I wasn't getting the horse work.'

He was chatting about this one day with the husband of one

of his few horse clients and was given some excellent advice: start hunting. 'That was in 1950. I duly had a horse and kept it in the garage when it wasn't out in the field with a New Zealand rug. I had never hunted before, and I've never stopped since – I completed my 43rd season last year, never missed a season, and did thirty-one days last season. In 1980 I became Master of the Teme Valley Foxhounds and continued for the next eleven years or so – I'm still chairman now. It's a small, friendly sort of hunt: on a regular day it's just the huntsman, me and thee sort of business; on a Saturday we might get a dozen.

'The moment I started to hunt, I started to get to know people. And the moment I started to get to know people and they knew I could look after horses, I got work. And then that moved on to their cattle work as well and the practice started to grow. In about 1951 or 1952 we took on an assistant here for the first time.'

But at about the same time Terry suddenly realised that – calamity! – his was a *sheep* practice, not a horse and cattle practice at all. 'There were thousands of the confounded things all over the place, and I knew nothing about sheep! My first lambing season in Montgomery was disastrous; they were dying right, left and centre after I'd lambed them. I had to do something about it and decided that I'd try caesareans. I knew how to do that on a bitch and started searching the literature about how to do it on ewes. Well, I couldn't find anything. So I messed about with the ewes and after two or three we found a way to do the caesarean on them and had great success with it. Later we developed it into a twenty-minute technique.

'Then a deputation of local farmers came to see me and said, "Look here, we're very sorry, Mr Boundy, we love you and we think your wife's a wonderful person, but you don't know anything about sheep. We think it would be a good idea if you kept some sheep yourselves. We'll each sell you three sheep." So we started with nine Kerry sheep and soon had a flock of fifty ewes. In looking after them I began to realise that the essence of sheep-keeping was that you had to feed them properly.'

Local breeders and shepherds willingly passed on their own deep knowledge of husbandry and feeding, and he soon appreciated the value of this new practical knowledge in the context of his profession: 'We began to realise that we could do a lot more work if the farmer would bring the sheep *in*. We let it be known that they could bring them in at any time of the day or night; we slept in the front room and if they hadn't got a telephone they could just throw a stone at the window and we'd be down.'

He devised other simple means of communication as well: 'When I went out on jobs ten miles or so away, my wife and I had an agreement: if there was an emergency call on the phone while I was out she would ring someone along the way and they would hang a towel over the gate. Whenever I saw a flapping towel, I'd stop and get the message.

'My wife used to come out with me on any operations. Attitudes were changing. When I went back to Tuckey in Whitchurch in 1946 before coming to Montgomery, Cheshire farmers would ring Tuckey and say, "Mr Boundy came with his wife to cleanse a cow the other day, Mr Tuckey. We didn't like Mrs Boundy to be there when a cow's being cleansed."

'In Montgomery, she would help me with calving cases late at night. You'd finish at one o'clock in the morning, and every time you'd have to go into the house and the wife was cutting sandwiches and there'd be a ham and all that. And you'd be sitting down to a ruddy great meal in the middle of the night.'

The sheep side of the practice built up rapidly during the 1950s. The veterinary profession as a whole was not particularly interested in sheep at that time and Terry began to see that there was the potential to do a lot more. The nature of his own practice was changing and it was time to stop operating in the garage and build his surgery and yard at Killaganoon. Later in the 1950s he was lucky enough to have a new assistant:

'A brilliant veterinary surgeon, Michael Harry Cross: he came from Liverpool, great chap; he stayed with me for a number of years until he decided he wanted to go into the church. We did a tremendous amount of sheep work together in those years, and as it all developed we would get perhaps a dozen vehicles waiting – there'd be sheep waiting for operations all the time, and we'd never move out of the surgery from seven in the morning to seven at night. My hands would be like pieces of raw meat.

'In about 1958 a girl by the name of Anne Lloyd wrote to me and said that she wanted to come into agricultural practice. This was practically unknown in Wales. I wouldn't like to say she was the first, but she was one of the first. She came to see us: a well built girl, well built from the ground upwards; a good set of shoulders on her and that, a bit of strength in her. So I said, "Righto, we'll take you on." She came as a student and then as an assistant. She was a very good practitioner; she thought a lot of the animals and treated them in a kind way. The farmers came to appreciate her. She was a great character: she invariably knew everything that was going on in the area because as soon as she finished a job she'd be in the house talking to the wives over a cup of tea. She worked hard, too.

'One night I'd been out all day on heavy work. The calving cows generally came in at about eleven o'clock and it was Mick Cross's night off. I said to Anne, "Do you mind going and doing a calving?" She said she'd love to do it – it was one of the first I'd sent her out to do by herself. And of course it was old Hugh Davis's, up the road, great character. I saw her the next morning and she said there had been no problems, it was all fine, fine. About a week later, on a Saturday night, I went down to the pub as usual and there was Hugh; he was a ten-pint-a-night and sixty-cigarettes-a-day man (he died when he was fifty-five). "Bounty," he says (he always pronounced it with a "t", not a "d"), "come 'ere, Bounty. Pint?" "Yes, thank you, yes, I'll have a pint. How's the calf going on?" "Oh fine, fine," he said, "but don't you send that lady again, please don't send her again." I said, "Why? What's the matter with her? She did the job." "I know, Bounty, but you know, it was very late at night and I had been in the Bell and had a few, mark you, and I came back and went down the cow house and this cow was calving and I knew I couldn't manage it. And you sent her. Well," he said, "she took her coat off, and then she took her jersey off and then," he said, "she took her shirt off. And there she was, standing beside me, fine figure of a woman and she'd only got a brazzery on. Well, we both put the ropes on the calf and we were pulling and I could feel her flesh up against my arm. And, you know, Bounty – don't you send her again: I will not be able to trust myself!" And that's a true story.'

Eventually Terry Boundy's Montgomery practice had five veterinarians. He came out of the partnership in 1980, by which time his reputation had become international. Meanwhile he had taken on various honorary and advisory roles, including being Senior Veterinary Officer for the Royal Welsh Agricultural Society for many years. Although he had begun his career working with horses and cattle, it is for his work with sheep that he is best known today: he has risen to high office in the sheep world, in which he has received several major awards. In due course he was also awarded an MBE for his services to agriculture for over thirty years.

In 1974 he went to the Antipodes but he didn't travel in style: the flight to New Zealand was in company with thirty horses – a collection of Morgans, Appaloosas and Quarter Horses with a few English Thoroughbreds. He travelled the length and breadth of

New Zealand and Australia and became involved for many years with post-graduate sheep management courses in Sydney.

In the 1970s he attended equine conferences in Dallas, Texas, making many new friends there, and in due course he found himself on the American lecture circuit in several states. He has been across the Atlantic at least a dozen times since then, though he has occasionally had trouble going through Customs with an electric ram ejaculator and an orchidometer!

'On another occasion I put my wallet down at some little airport somewhere and it vanished – it had about $500 in it. A few days later we were having one of the regular breakfast sessions for vets at 7.30 in the morning and one of the staff brought me a package. There was my wallet, with the $500 intact and all my credit cards, with a scribbled note that said: "When I discovered you were an English veterinarian, I could not steal your wallet because I have read *All Creatures Great and Small*."'

Terry is determined to make the most of his fifty years of experience: in his mid-seventies now, he teaches final-year students at Liverpool and still works locally with his horse clients and his sheep consultancy. 'Oh, I wouldn't give up practising – not yet! And I'll go on teaching and working as long as I am capable of doing so. Because it is my *life*.'

Despite his travels, this busy, busy man always found time for his beloved hunting, enjoying every season even now. 'Looking back, there have been so many times that I've enjoyed myself enormously. I loved my army career; I love my hunting and shall hunt as long as I possibly can. I don't think I ever enjoyed a day so much as the one when Her Majesty the Queen gave me the MBE. But the finest thrill of all my life was in 1988 when I took the Teme Valley Foxhounds round the ring at the Royal Welsh in front of a crowd of about 60,000 people. That was the day in my life which I would love to do all over again, if I could.'

Chickens, chimps and halibut

ooooo

The Victorian house faces what is perhaps Europe's largest area of common land: Sutton Park, a typical mixture of heather, scrubby birch and pine stretching to apparently distant horizons. It is hard to believe that Birmingham is so close: there is no sign of urbanisation.

The garden is overgrown: it is a wildlife haven, and foxes have bred in it for at least half a century. A huge monkey puzzle and other feature trees dominate the back garden. They were planted when the house was built in 1897, and the house, with its large airy rooms, has not changed greatly during its life.

Mary Brancker is a woman of presence, great assurance, warmth and immense good humour. Her short, somewhat wiry grey hair had been long and golden when she was a child, and that is recalled in the direct blue of her eyes. She has a strong profile, with a splendid nose that suits her down-to-earthness, but a warm smile frequently lights up her face. She has the most infectious laugh you can imagine, a deep throaty sound that bursts out joyously and often. She is not by nature a serious person, even though she has gone right to the very top of her profession.

She was born in 1914 in Hampstead, though her parents came from Lancashire and Cheshire and her natural feelings remain for that part of the country. The family on her father's side were mostly businessmen, teachers, mathematicians; on her mother's side, too, they were professional people, especially lawyers, but they were also 'very, very animal-minded: they loved the country but they were not farmers or land-owners.' It was from her mother's family that Mary inherited her own passionate love of animals.

They had cats and dogs at home until she was about six years old, when they moved into a flat in the centre of London. What could an animal-loving child do about that? Goldfish and budgerigars were not common then but she was a resourceful person. She asked her parents if she could keep worms. And her father said only if she could guarantee he would never meet them crawling around the place, which she could not.

Her father died the following year, at the age of only forty-two, a week after her seventh birthday, and they moved to a cheap house in the country near Farnham, Surrey, 'which was heaven'. Friends gave them a cat and a dog. Best of all, her grandmother gave the children half-a-crown each with which to buy animals; Mary bought a female rabbit, and being a thoroughly practical person, she persuaded her sister, who was not animal-minded, to buy a male rabbit.

By the age of twelve Mary wanted to be a farmer but her family pointed out that they didn't have the kind of money to buy a farm. She toyed with the idea of being a zoo-keeper but dismissed the idea of being a veterinary surgeon because she did not want to hurt animals. Three years later her headmistress gave her a list of ten possibilities for her future career. They were all jobs that were just right for a caring child with an interest in nature, like Mary, but at first she rejected the lot. Thinking again, she looked at one of them: veterinary work. To that she said, 'Perhaps.'

She entered veterinary college when she left school. There were only five veterinary schools in those days (London, Liverpool, Glasgow, Edinburgh and Dublin) and not all were happy to accept women. Edinburgh in particular was against them, claiming that there were not enough toilets. Mary became an undergraduate at the Royal Veterinary College in Camden Town, where the buildings were literally falling down. She thoroughly enjoyed everything about it, including the social life: there were only ten girls among the eighty students of Mary's year.

Like all students she saw practice with various veterinary surgeons, including Dr Blount, in Hastings, who was ahead of his time and had studied poultry. In those days the colleges taught nothing at all about poultry, and very little about pigs or sheep. Blount was actually in general practice, involved in poultry as a sideline because he could see that they would soon become highly commercial, and he ran a diagnostic laboratory. Mary returned to college really interested in the subject and made a point of learning more. Fortunately there was an anatomy lecturer who also saw ahead and taught them about the anatomy of poultry.

'I'd just had time to do a certain amount of practical poultry work when the war came, and the government saw that poultry was a way of feeding the population, so they began to subsidise the advice given to poultry farmers and offered them free tests and so on. I did some work on that after the war but it had become a government thing, not a veterinary one – the whole business had been lost to the profession because we had not had the sense to say that we knew something about poultry.' That taught Mary a valuable lesson for later life, and would be the spur to her interest in some other unusual species in due course.

As students, their practical lessons included shoeing horses. Horse work was still very important and the students spent time at the large stables for railway horses next to the college, learning how to identify lame horses, how to cast them with ropes into a prone position for operations, and how to restrain a restless horse by picking up one of its front feet so that, in theory, it didn't have enough legs to stand on to kick you.

Before leaving college in 1937, Mary proclaimed that she hated London so much that she would rather be unemployed for a year than work in it. But it was a time of high unemployment for everybody, let alone women, and she wrote endlessly in response to advertisements. Meanwhile her locum work included a major practice in Paddington where she was given the use of a small Fiat with no starting handle and an unreliable self-starter: the easiest technique was to put her foot through the driver's door and scoot. In another practice, she discovered that a large number of farmers took advantage of a tremendous thunderstorm: they suddenly wanted veterinary certificates to the effect that their animals had been struck by lightning, so they could put in insurance claims blaming the lightning for sheep which were in fact already dead, cows already not in milk and horses that were already lame.

It happened that, as a student, she had seen practice in Tamworth with the dynamic Harry Steel-Bodger and, after one or two false starts, she returned to Tamworth as an assistant at the Sutton branch of the practice, seven miles away. By now the war was imminent:

'I lived over the practice in Sutton, doing morning and evening surgeries there and any visits, but I went over to Tamworth as well, where I was responsible for our big boarding kennels and the hospital. What I really liked, of course, was farm practice but there wasn't any in Sutton: it was kept as a rather high-class small animal branch. It was only when I was over at Tamworth that sometimes a call would come in when everyone else was out, or they'd bring a sheep in or something, and I always jumped at the chance.

'Actually there was just one farm in Sutton but it was a very sad situation: they only had ten acres and the farmer had a brain tumour. The wife was trying to cope with the farm – some cows, a couple of pigs and a few hens – and bring up two small boys at the same time. They owed us some money, which didn't bother us but she felt badly about it. Well, there was a great dearth of eggs at the beginning of the war, so the arrangement was that I should call there once a month and pick up a dozen eggs at a time until she had wiped out her debt.

'I would examine each of her half-a-dozen cows when I came for the eggs, and I examined them right through their pregnancies. If they needed any form of treatment, we'd discuss costs, but I examined them and gave information from the examination for free because it taught me as I went along. And so we became friendly and found we could do something for each other: she began to talk about me to neighbouring smallholders, and that was how the nucleus started. And no, they didn't all pay me in eggs, it was good hard cash!

'They were all ex-servicemen smallholdings; Birmingham had bought the land after World War I and gave ex-servicemen ten acres for a start. When her two lads grew up, her holding was given to another ex-serviceman from World War II, and he wouldn't have me to start with. But one evening I got a call: he had been losing all his little pigs and could I come and explain why. He only had two sows: one had lost all her litter and the second one's were dying, and his wife was in bed with 'flu; everything was going wrong. This was in about 1950, I suppose. He went into pigs in a big way after that, feeding them on swill, and was soon fattening a thousand pigs on that ten-acre holding. When I finally retired from large animal practice in 1970, this same man had just bought his fifth farm and was still my client.

'I used to vaccinate all his pigs – a revolting job on swill pigs but the money was superb! He did it all very intelligently: he collected from the abattoir and the bakeries and balanced it all properly. And he always got top marks for his pigs. He had left school at fourteen but he was a good businessman. When he developed back trouble and retired early, he told me: "Do you know, I'm making more money than the prime minister!"

'I post-mortemed all his pigs for a year, every one that died, and he watched me closely then at the end of the year he said, "Right, I've got the picture, and if I open them myself I shall know whether I need to send for you or whether it's just one of those things." Which was entirely sensible. Once we were doing a postmortem in a nissen hut and it was dark. He opened the boiler, great big flames; he got hold of the pig fore and aft, swung it in and said, "That's the way to get rid of the wife!"'

Mary looks back with great affection to her early days in the Tamworth practice. 'Everything was *fun*!' She then began a lifetime's involvement in what might be described as the politics of the veterinary world, sitting on various British Veterinary Association councils. In about 1940 she and others started a women's society, which would continue for some fifty years.

After seven years as Harry Steel-Bodger's assistant, she became a partner in the practice; and that was how it stayed until 'S-B' became seriously ill in 1951. She has countless tales from large animal practice, sometimes involving falling into the slurry pit or 'sock' (the farm cesspit) and frequently ending with injuries of some kind. There was the time when she examined a large sow, lying on its side with an abscess on its back foot. The sow objected, lashed out with the affected foot and spilt her eyebrow, giving her a permanent scar. Then she had the terrifying experience of being cornered by a Friesian bull: it was being held by a bull-staff, which broke, and she had no escape route. So she stayed still. The roof of the bullpen was too low for him to toss her but he charged her instead. She was leaning against a gate and the cowman quickly opened it; she fell out, the bull hesitated and the cowman slammed the gate in his face – but she already had the imprints of the bull's horns across her front and of the gate across her back. Ah well, the imprints faded after a week. Then in 1947 she contracted brucellosis, for which the treatment at the time was more dangerous than the disease itself, although the diagnosis was almost a relief as it had been suggested that she might have had a brain tumour. She felt so ill that it demanded all her willpower and energy to drag herself from case to case. The treatment, in the end, was to give up everything except her work and to rest as much as possible. And it succeeded, though it was a most depressing experience and it was not until the summer of 1949 that she was fully active again.

Mary had planned to give up farm practice by her early forties but somehow she forgot to do so until she had reached her mid-fifties. Then she tried to interest her cat and dog clients in preventive medicine but not all of them were grateful. 'I remember a poodle coming in to have its nails clipped and going out with a diagnosis of diabetes – and they thought that was my fault! They really were not interested in preventive medicine.'

Small animal practice had other drawbacks. She was checking out a young alsatian for fleas one day when he 'imbedded his fang tooth in my hand, turned it sideways and pulled it out, leaving an inch-long tear in my flesh.' Furthermore, Mary was beginning to find herself getting increasingly irritated by the small animal side of things – although she had developed several other interests in the meantime. For example, there was her zoo work. 'I was lucky there. Somebody once said to me, "You have been terribly lucky – everything just drops into your lap." But I said, "No I simply sit with my hands out, catching things." And I think there's a lot in that: you see an opportunity and you take it. Even so, it was by pure chance and a series of lucky breaks that I'd seen practice at Tamworth with S-B, and that he was a chap who treated absolutely anything he was asked to treat. And in those pre-war days quite a few people kept odd small exotic pets like monkeys. I had always been fascinated by them and so it *was* a bit of luck that I saw practice with him.

'Immediately after the war, I was called in by two women in Sutton who ran a pet shop; they had some monkeys for sale, but these had contracted TB; I managed to get them right but the women had enough conscience to know that they could not sell the animals. And these became a nucleus. They went and bought a baby chimp, which at that time was quite a common thing do – people were starved for pets because of the war and it was very easy to get hold of chimps. They are fascinating creatures and quite a number were being sold. And quasi-scientific people were trying to bring them up as children in the house, that sort of thing.

'Anyway, these two women in Sutton thought that this one chimp of theirs was lonely, so they bought a second one; but the animals began to grow until the women realised they could not live over the shop any longer. By this time people were asking them to bring their chimps to open garden parties.

'They were both genuinely into animals; they ran the pet shop commercially, they bred dogs and so forth. So they moved to a village about six miles away. The chimps by this time were becoming a dangerous size but they said that, having been brought up as children in the house, it wasn't fair to put them outside so they gave them a suite built on to the bungalow. In the meantime I continued to look after them. Then they began to make a bit of money opening fêtes and things with them and people began to hear about them and to go and see them at weekends. Then somebody else came back with a chimp they'd sold and discovered it wasn't happy, so they brought it back and gave it to them. So they had three chimps.

'Then they heard that there was an orang and so they bought that, and they still had the original TB monkeys. By now their relatives, who lived across the road, issued an edict: either they must curtail their activities (because the whole situation was getting out of hand and the lane was packed with cars at the weekend), or they must move and start a zoo. So they started Twycross Zoo.

'I continued with this zoo work for several years; I went on doing it for a time after I'd retired from practice. They set up a Trust for the zoo, for financial security when they die, and I'm on its council. We've still got some animals over there that are more than forty years old. I said to the keeper the other day, "They don't show their age." (Some of them go a little grey, but they don't seem to go thin like humans do.) And I asked the keepers if they noticed any difference. They roared with laughter and said, "Yes – they come in and have a kip in the afternoons!"

'All of the apes and some of the monkeys recognise me, and I notice that a lot of the young chimps greet me now, though I've never treated any of them. The keeper said, "But they have noticed that their elders and betters greet you!" Mind you, they are all extremely dangerous. The only thing to be said for chimps is that you can divert them much more easily than the others. Once an orang has made up its mind about something, you can't change it.'

That she should have become involved with exotic animals is typical of Mary Brancker; she has boundless curiosity and cannot resist a challenge, and is forever looking for fields in which no vet has ever trodden before. A surprising interest came to her back in the 1960s and that was fish; in fact, this was why I had so much wanted to talk to her: I had read her chapter in a book on aquaculture in which she talked about halibut, and the voice that came through was one that was immensely compassionate, even about a fish. She talked about them as individual animals that responded to kindness and to gentle handling. A mature breeding halibut can grow to be six feet long; but still, I had never really thought of fish as individuals. So why fish, of all creatures?

'Well, remember what I said about poultry, how the veterinary profession had missed the boat on that, back in my student days in the 1930s? When I discovered in 1966 that fish had been developed for potential farming, I didn't want the same thing to happen. I had no interest in fish at all as an animal, and I didn't even like them to eat. But at the time I was president of the British Veterinary Association ...'

This casual passing remark is typical of Mary: she had held the most important position in the profession and had failed to mention it before. We'd return to that subject later.

'... at a time when you had to attend endless drinks parties, which were dull and monotonous. And I discovered that a good talking point was: "Do you realise we have now developed fish as a potential farmed animal and the veterinary profession is very interested?" This left people gasping, but they didn't know what questions to ask! One or two of them said, "Tell us more!" But I didn't *know* any more, so I thought I had better find out. I was introduced to someone in the White Fish Authority, who said the only way to do so was to go and see it in action.

'Right, but at the end of a three-year spell as an officer of the BVA I was *completely* broke and the practice needed a lot of care and attention. And the thought of going up to Scotland, the cost in time and money ... but I took a deep breath, and up I went. They showed me round and I always remember they showed me two dustbins (as I recollect) and the chappy said, "This lot we are looking at, they actually were weaned a fortnight before that lot you have just looked at, but they've never done well – there was a storm the night I weaned them and it upset them and set them back." And I thought, this is exactly the same as pigs! What fun! It's just doing it in water, which makes it much more exciting!

'They are smashing people up there, where the research is going on about these fish. One of them is a natural stockman, though he doesn't know it. If I say I want to do something with one of his fish, I have to go through a whole cross-examination: is it really essential? Will it hurt it? I went up once and there was a sort of gloom over the place: "Hannibal died yesterday." Hannibal! But they are quite practical: the next day they ate Hannibal.'

Farm animals, cats and dogs, primates, fish: whatever next?

'I'm now working on invertebrates. I did tortoises for a bit but too many people jumped on that bandwagon and it was getting too popular and too scientific, so I wanted to think of something else. There has been a gradual move over the last ten years to keeping stick insects and tarantulas and things, and John Cooper and I thought the veterinary profession should be prepared to look at them. There was a BSAVA conference early in 1993 and one day we had a press conference and I was invited to talk about invertebrates as pets. Well, there were a whole lot of high-powered speakers at the conference, all very good and above my head – and way above the press's head. So I gave a short talk, and then came the questions. "How would I know if my invertebrate needs to be taken to the veterinary surgeon?" "Well," I said, "if your wife comes down to breakfast, you don't need to ask her how she feels: you can look across the table and know if she is feeling low. And your dog, you don't need to ask. So if you have a proper rapport with your tarantula ..." The press loved that! And, don't tell a soul, I don't actually like spiders!'

Oh yes, that small matter of the presidency of the BVA. That was in 1967, and Mary was their first ever woman president: the job took up five days a week for a year, with the year before that as a warm-up as Junior Vice President, and the following year as Senior Vice President. In 1969 Mary Brancker was awarded the OBE, which she so richly deserved.

RIST.
41
NEWSAGEN

PONYMAN OF THE NEW FOREST

ooooo

Jack Broughton has lived in the New Forest since 1951, but he has never slowed down to Forest ways: he is a vigorous man, an outdoor man, whose mind is constantly racing and whose words do their best to keep up as he jumps with enthusiasm from one subject to another. He is way over on the far side of the fields supervising a mechanical digger, but there is a warm greeting from his golden retriever, Ben, in the yard in front of a house set amid open paddocks. There are stables around the yard: this is clearly a man whose first interest is in horses.

Jack's background had no agricultural connection at all, not even with horses, but he was always 'mad on animals'. As a child he created his own ha'penny museum, charging other children half a penny to come and see his exhibits. He would buy reptiles and amphibians from a shop in Manchester called 'Wilds' – terrapins, snakes, lizards and tree frogs – and would collect whatever he could from the countryside. With the money he made from his ha'pennies, he would buy more exhibits, 'anything that was alive and could fit into a small glasshouse attached to our house'. At school in Bolton, Lancashire, he gave talks on British animal life, complete with live exhibits.

'Obviously I wanted to do something with animals,' says Jack. 'I seemed to be cut out for it from the word go. Even before I had the museum, I had my farm set when other people had Meccano. Whenever my parents went anywhere, they would bring back those little metal cows, the lead pigs and sheep for my farm. I had tremendous patience with animals but not machines. Anything mechanical I detested. I'd kick my bicycle with wrath if it went wrong. Being interested in animals I decided to write to Julian Huxley, the naturalist of the day, when I was about fifteen; I told him I was interested in animals, especially butterflies and moths, and asked if he could suggest a career in entomology? He told me not to go for entomology because most of my time woud be spent working out how to kill the creatures. And he asked, what about being a veterinary surgeon?'

The idea had never occurred to Jack, and certainly not to his parents, who had hoped he would become a doctor. However, in 1942 he went to Liverpool University and qualified from there as a veterinary surgeon in 1947.

He saw practice for a while in Birmingham, where he was allowed to do things like spaying cats. His mentor was 'very short-sighted and not very good at it himself, so it didn't take us long to be more adept than he was'. He spent quite a while in a practice at Bury, where the vet had bought one of the first X-ray machines to be seen after the war. Then he saw practice in Bolton, in the days when there were still a lot of heavy horses around. That took him back to his childhood:

'The milkman came every morning with a horse, the coalman came with a horse, the baker had a horse. I used to go out and help deliver the milk two roads down with the horse – they were glad to have any of the kids doing that. You ladled the milk from the churn, walked down to the door with the ladle and poured the milk into the jug they'd left in the porch. And the horse knew exactly where to stop each time.'

Finally he saw quite a lot of horse practice in Ireland after the war was over. During the war he had been in a reserve occupation, of course, but had still spent a lot of time in uniform and on various military courses: he learned to drive in the army and, more important perhaps, he also learned to ride. Another course, at Doncaster, concerned mules, which they would ride.

'In the army we raced them bareback over straw bales. Some of them bucked you off as soon as you got on; some were so placid that they would not go at all. I knew of one veterinary surgeon with a practice in Southampton, name of Edwards, who was in the army in Burma during the war. On one occasion the Japs were closing in on them and they came to a fork in the way; they couldn't for the life of them work out which one to take. If it was the wrong one, they'd walk straight into the Japs. They had a mule with them as a pack animal and they decided to let it go. And it led them the right way, the safe way.'

A year after qualifying, he spent two very happy years in an agricultural practice in Whitchurch, Shropshire, where he was introduced to hunting. He bought a horse, a good jumper, and became interested in local show jumping and hunter trials – anything that was within hacking distance. He enjoyed himself in Whitchurch.

'In the very early days there, we had quite a lot of doctoring to do. The local doctor was expected to know how to calve a cow, and it was not unusual when *we* visited a farm for them to say, "Would you take a look at Grandpa while you're here?" You get a wide range of surgery being a vet, more so than doctors because they tend to specialise, whereas vets operate on virtually any part of the anatomy. And a bladder's a bladder, an eye's an eye, whether it belongs to a dog or to a human being. All the same, really.

'Of course, a human can tell a doctor that if he has to have an injection he wants it done very nicely and painlessly. But if you inject an animal and you don't make a proper job, the animal's apt to kick you or bite you. Perhaps the doctors might learn more quickly if their patients turned around and thumped them on the kneecap when they didn't give an injection properly!

'There is an art in injecting, especially with horses. If you get a big horse and you upset it, you're going to have a rough time, it's going to be bashing around the stable, and the next time it sees you coming it's not going to like you at all. But if you can fool it and get the needle in quietly without it knowing, then you're quids in. Animals have very good memories connected with pain and discomfort.'

One day there was a phone call: 'Can you come and have a look: I've got a lame zebra.' Oh yes, thought Jack. Friends were always ringing up with funny remarks like that. While he was trying to work out whose voice it was, he said, 'And I suppose you've got an elephant with stomach ache as well!' There was a pause, and then the caller said, 'Look, do you or don't you want to come and look at my zebra?' 'Hang on,' said Jack, 'have you really got a zebra?' 'Yes, we're Roberts Circus, we've just arrived in Whitchurch, we want to put on a show tonight and one of our zebras is lame. Would you come and have a look at it?' So he went round, apologising.

'When I arrived, they told me: "Watch it. They are very good at hitting you with their heads, zebras." It was lame in a front leg, so I was careful to watch its head as I picked up the leg. It promptly kicked me in the backside with the hindleg!'

After Whitchurch he went to Nottingham with the intention ultimately of becoming a partner.

'I went to attend a dog in a terraced house one day. People sat at the table, having tea, and I examined the dog, not taking much notice of them. I went out to the car to collect a syringe and then went back indoors. I perched myself on the edge of the table as they had their meal and started to fill my hypodermic syringe. There was complete silence. Then someone pointed at me and stuttered, "Who ... who ... who are you?" I looked up and saw these mesmerised people staring at me. I looked for the dog. There wasn't one. I was in the wrong house! They must have been terrified, a complete stranger walking in and calmly filling a hypodermic!'

He had an excellent job, with good income and good prospects, and he liked the vet he was working for, but he was not entirely happy, working in a city and dealing mainly with small animals. He and his horse greatly missed the type of hunting country around Whitchurch. After nine months he decided it was time to move and found himself joining a practice at Ringwood, Hampshire. It was pure chance that brought him to the area, but in fact he had always had a yen for it, ever since he had been youth hostelling and had stayed a couple of nights there, talking to the New Forest ponies. So when the opportunity came, he jumped at it.

In theory he was to have worked his way towards taking over the practice himself in eighteen months' time but in the event one partner had a sudden stroke and died almost before Jack returned home from the interview, and the other left. So he went straight into it on his own. 'It was very run down. I think I had about one dog in my first fortnight.'

Gradually the work started to come in, though it would be a while before Jack knew anything about the ways of the Forest, let alone the dialect: 'There was this cow with what they called "lure". I'd no idea what they meant. Of course, when I asked, "What is lure?", he said, "Thought you were a vet. It's in its foot." Then I realised it was the local name for foul in the foot.'

And he began to meet some interesting people. 'There was this wonderful woman, an expert on folklore, and she was married to a sculptor. The first time I called in to see them was late on a lovely moonlit summer's night. She said she would meet me at Stony Cross because they lived in a caravan tucked away in the Forest and I wouldn't be able to find it otherwise. When

I reached Stony Cross I was flagged down by a woman whose hair seemed to come almost down to her ankles; she had rings all the way up her arms and looked extraordinary. She *was* extraordinary, very well educated and well spoken. They had come up from Cornwall in this caravan. I'd been called to see her greyhound which had chased a buck and the animal had swung round and cut the dog with its antlers. So I stitched him up and then on this lovely warm night we had a cup of tea, brewed on a tripod over an open fire outside.

'Now, she had this obsession with animals that were black and white and she tried to start a zoo full of them – Gloucester Old Spot pigs, zebras, Appaloosa horses (she was trying to cross them with the zebras), skunks – anything black and white.'

Jack became something of a workaholic and the practice began to take off remarkably fast, so much so that, after a year, he was exhausted and in desperate need of an assistant.

It was the period when tuberculin testing of cattle was just coming in and he'd had the unenviable task of testing Dalgety's herd of 300 black Galloway cows. The animals ran the Forest; they were very wild and were frequently knocked down on the roads by passing vehicles. 'So I knew this herd would be a difficult job. We started at daybreak and worked into the dark. You couldn't drive them: they'd turn on you, and the worst ones were the last to come in. We had to throw bales of lighted hay to get them to move into the crush.'

There were lighter moments, of course, and there is another story concerning the Dalgety herd. 'Anthrax is, of course, a notifiable disease: if an animal died and you didn't know why, it was mandatory on the farmer to ensure that it wasn't anthrax. We'd have to go out and take a blood smear and we had to make sure that the area from which the blood was taken was cauterised because the spores can live a hundred years and if they get into the soil you'll have trouble at a later date.

'On this occasion one of the Dalgety animals had died, down here at Linford, and I went out to it on a cold, crisp winter's night. I took my sample and then I cauterised it in the normal way by throwing methylated spirits over the area and then putting a match to it. But I threw on a bit too much meths and because the coat was dry and standing up it caught fire – the whole side of the dead cow went up in flames.

'Now, it just happened that there was a courting couple in a car about a hundred yards away. As I came back to my car, they said, "What's that? What's happening?" Jokingly I said, "Ah, black magic!" and drove away.

'About eleven o'clock that night there was a knock on my door, and there stood a sergeant of the police. "Mr Broughton," he said, "we've had an extraordinary thing. Some excited people came in and said there was black magic going on in the Forest, they'd taken the car number and the man had rushed off, and we've traced the car number and it's yours!" "Right, sergeant," I said, "what was I doing?" "Well," he said, "you were setting fire to a cow." "Yes," I said, "that's right. And what could I be doing which would involve me setting fire to a cow in the Forest?" "I've no idea," he said.'

Then there was his session of tuberculin testing on a smallholding. At the end of the test, one cow seemed to be missing. The smallholder thought he must have overlooked her in the field; off he went to find her while Jack hung around waiting. He returned without the cow: 'There's no sign of her. I couldn't have lost her on the road. And she's not here. Can't think where she's gone.' Jack finished testing the rest of the herd and went into the house to wash his hands.

'I came out with a big grin on my face. I told him: "I've found your cow!" "What do you mean, you've found my cow?" he said.

And I told him: it was in the dining-room. All the time we were looking for it, the cow was in the house.'

Now that he had an assistant, he was able to build up the practice in both large and small animals. 'I liked to have a bit of everything, a balance. In a mixed practice your winter work was cattle; in the summer, when they were harvesting, the farmers were not so keen to see you, but it happened that the horse work and small animal work accelerated at that stage, so we were well balanced. But we had so much farm work that a lot of the small animal work had to be done in the evening. We worked until very late, often doing operations at midnight. Bitch whelping in those days meant taking it into the house and being up most of the night with it. And after operations, we'd sit up with it in front of the fire trying to help if it was a touch-and-go thing like pyometry. Colic, you'd stay with that until it was better and probably missed a night's sleep; but you still had to be out early the next morning all the same, to test cows. And we didn't have any of today's excellent tranquillisers, so your animal handling had to be pretty good then.

'It's changed a lot now – it's comparatively easy. But it is becoming too much of a science and not enough of an art. That is one reason I particularly like the horse world. You either get on with horses, and they with you, or you don't.'

In 1958 they bought the present farm and stocked it with New Forest ponies and cattle. Jack was too busy to farm at that stage and his wife looked after the cattle and calves. He had met Jean at an agricultural ball in Ireland and she had quickly settled into helping him to run the practice.

'It's very important to have someone as excellent as she is. Having someone who was a good administrator allowed me to concentrate very much on what I wanted to do, which was treating the animals. And there was no one I'd prefer to help me with an operation, say, a caesarian section on a bitch. She'd help with the large animals, too – pulling out calves, rumenotomies. The only thing she was a bit squeamish about was punching a tooth out through the sinus, or having to remove an eye.

'Then there was the farming: she did all of that, because I simply didn't have the time. I remember when we brought down eleven West Highland cattle from Oban; I think they were the first of that breed in the Forest. They arrived at Ringwood station on a day when my wife was in hospital. I rushed up to her in the ward saying, "They've come! They've come!" "Who's come?" she asked. "The Highlands!" "Oh," she said, "and incidentally, I've just had our second son."

'We ran the Highlands on the Forest, but the area didn't have grids then and they would get down into Ringwood and startle people, peering through shop windows. They do have very long horns! We had an old-timer, Mr Martin, working on the farm for us and he'd go down to Ringwood with a big sack of hay on his back and march them all the way back to Linford. Then I tried putting them into a trailer and taking them in two lots up to the old aerodrome at Fritham. I turned the trailer round and round and round so as to confuse them before letting them out. But it only took them twenty-four hours to get back here, mooing away merrily!

'All the children helped with the farm: they all did their fair stint, especially with the ponies. My wife hadn't ridden until she came here but after a while she was riding and both my eldest sons fell off a horse before they were born! They kept their interest in horses – the girls, too.' The family is possibly unique in that most of them, though not Jean, are keen polo players.

'I think I must have started playing in about 1960. Why? Because some client of mine said I ought to and he offered to take me and my pony over in his trailer. Well, that pony was no good at all for it, but then I found that my other one, an old horse called Robin, was an incredible player – you only get one of those in a lifetime. He was terrifically good at colt hunting, and was soon a lot better at polo than I was: he used to get very fed up with me sometimes. He was clever, and he had a great sense of humour. Poor old Mr Martin couldn't get on with him at all, and would have a terrible time; he was a bit scared of him, and the horse knew it. And if there was someone on his back who was new to him he loved to get halfway down a slope and pick his spot to act the fool. He liked his bit of fun, but he was a good character and I had him for years and years.

Most of his horses have been good to him and he feels he has been lucky. 'Horses have a particularly good memory for routes. When I first came here I used to get lost in the Forest but if I didn't know which way to turn I'd leave it to my mare and she'd always get me back. They have a great homing instinct. And they are such individuals, they are characters – that's what makes it so interesting. What goes for one of my horses won't go for another. Some might enjoy polo or hunting, but some of them don't and if they don't like it they won't play. It is the same with jumping: some just don't like it and are no good at it, others take to it and enjoy it. They are not stupid animals at all.'

There came a time when Jack felt that his practice was too successful; he therefore decided to concentrate on horse work, but he was still run off his feet. Finally he sold the whole practice to his partner. Now he concentrates on consultancy work and a host of honorary jobs in shows, the polo world and so on; but he still keeps his hand in with second opinions.

'I would not want to retire completely. And I'm interested in wildlife conservation, as well: I go down to the Avon Forest Sanctuary at St Leonards, where all sorts of things come in. Yesterday I saw a curlew, a seagull, a squirrel, a pigeon, a goose and a swan, and they will all be returned to the wild as soon as we have them fit again. Another day I might be dealing with hedgehogs, foxes, badgers – I never know what's going to come in and I just go along when they need me there.'

But horses remain his first love. Over the years he has studied the ways of them, especially the Forest ponies. 'We keep New Forest ponies; I felt as a vet you had to be involved so that you knew at first hand all the problems. And you are more likely to be in a position to correct the "good intentions" but bad effects of some people who don't really know what they are talking about, who don't keep them themselves. There is always a hooha about the condition of the ponies, for example. Of course they do lose condition over the winter and some actually do need to be taken off, but it's not easy to do so. If you want to get one mare off, it means a posse of horses to round her up and then she'll immediately go and join with a bunch of others so that you have to round the whole lot up. And that means galloping mares about which are heavily in foal – not a good thing. Left to their own devices, they usually have no problems foaling in the Forest: they just find themselves a nice quiet spot and get on with it.

'I was out in the Forest one day when I saw a mare starting to foal. She must have been an experienced old mare: she started to strain and all of a sudden, to my amazement, she fell on her side with a woomph! There was a big squelch and out popped the foal. I'm sure she did it quite deliberately, knowing that it would speed things up. She knew what she was doing.

'The New Forest stallions are so individualistic. Some are very strict disciplinarians and the mares don't move out of their patch in the Forest. Others hardly bother and just drift. Others indulge in wife-swapping. They can be very particular, too. I once had a couple of mares that ran down the bottom here, always together since yearlings, called Bunny and Rachel. A stallion, Broomy

Look Again, came down into the valley but he would only take Rachel: he would push Bunny away and she had to go off with a younger stallion (the younger ones pick up the left-overs). Every season that happened, and after the mating season the two mares would be back together again. As soon as Broomy Look Again left the area, they both went together with another stallion.

'Some of the stallions can be quite vicious to mares they don't like, especially if they are loose together in the field. They are all right until they are about five or six years old and then if they take a dislike to a mare they will beat her up – kick her and even kill a mare, because she can't escape from the field and gets cornered, or she tries to jump out and gets caught on the wire. Other stallions are perfectly all right with any animal, always. At the moment I have an Arab who is nice to every mare, very kind, and that passes on to his youngsters, that lovely temperament.'

Jack is deeply involved in the many affairs of the Forest and in its way of life, but a lot is changing. 'The biggest single change here is that there used to be smallholdings everywhere – a few milking cows, pigs, poultry – but that's all gone. I used to go round Burley from farm to farm to farm, but now they are all people's second homes, beautifully done up, with horses in railed paddocks. It's not the Foresters any more; they haven't been followed by their sons, and there seems to be no future for small farming unless you subsidise it as heavily as they do in France.'

He has been veterinary surgeon to the New Forest Pony and Cattle Breeders Society for some forty years, and also attends the Beaulieu Road Sales where he and another vet inspect every animal (some three hundred of them) to ensure that they are fit enough for sale and that the foals are not too immature. Before they can be sold at Beaulieu Road, the animals have to be rounded up from the Forest and this is the great event of 'colt-hunting': 'Much more fun than foxhunting! It is purposeful, it is a job, you are part of a team on horseback, you have an end product, and it is part of rural life. Polo ponies are ideal for colt-hunting because they are so good at twisting and turning.'

Out in the field, in full view of the house, are his polo ponies and his brood mares. He has only one pony running on the Forest at the moment; he has his Arab stallion running with some of his Argentinian polo mares, and he has some yearlings and half a dozen polo ponies.'

The little boy who used to buy exotic pets from a shop in Manchester and play with his little metal farm animals has never lost his love of animals and his fascination with natural history. 'It was my love of natural history that started me off and it has never waned. Birds I love, and I like to think I know every bird I see in the wild. On holiday I usually spend my time with a pair of binoculars. And we get a great variety of birds here: I always carry binoculars when I'm walking out with the dog across the Forest ... Quick! Look out there – it's a buzzard!' In fact there were two buzzards, right on cue, lazily circling against a deep evening-blue summer sky above the field.

'I love all wildlife. Badgers, foxes. I was coming home early one morning from a milk fever, a lovely spring morning, and decided to walk through some woods near Bisterne on private land. I looked over a little culvert and there was an otter. It didn't see me and I watched it rooting about in the mud for quite some time before it looked up at me and then shot off. It is the only one I have seen close to, and it's not something you see very often.

'I haven't really had enough time to indulge in my love of wildlife, with so much work, but I've been lucky in that my pleasures and the work merged: interests were all part of my work, it all merged one hundred per cent. It's a very chaotic life, a vet's life, and this is a thing that I think has to be emphasised: it's not a job. It's a way of life.'

AT THE DOUBLE ON DARTMOOR

ooooo

The road from Bovey Tracey is designated as a major one but in places it is dangerously narrow, almost single track, as it swings from side to side between rounded hills, many of them with blankets of trees spilling down to the valleys on the kinder reaches of Dartmoor. The fields are small hereabouts, on a properly human scale, and they are scattered with little outcrops of rock, like sculptures artlessly placed.

The moorland village of Moretonhampstead fits snugly into its environment, embracing a crossroads. The entrance to the home of Bob and Anne Pigott here is protected by a juicy-berried yew tree. There is a small surgery behind the house and a worried young boy arrives, carefully holding a wounded pigeon and seeking help. A fluffy ginger cat winds itself persuasively round my ankles as I tug at the knob that jangles the bell at the front door of the house. A bouncy and vaguely lopsided golden retriever offers a warm welcome and the generous present of his dug-up bone.

Anne Pigott, fair-haired and energetic, has the kettle already on the boil in the kitchen. Bob is equally energetic, a touch restless, a man who tends to do everything at the double, perhaps because he did his National Service in a regiment whose marching pace was the fastest in the army. He is not Devon born and bred, but his roots have been firmly transplanted in the county for more than half his lifetime and it is very much his home. He was actually born in Crouch End, London, in 1928, but four years later the family moved down to the south Hampshire coast, between Bournemouth and Christchurch, and that was his childhood home.

There was no family connection with the veterinary world at all but, as a boy of eleven, Bob began to work during his school holidays with a local veterinarian. He has no idea why he chose to do so but he was soon cycling five or six miles there early in the mornings. His boss was a man who would have been known to many of Bob's generation because he was an external examiner at the Royal Veterinary College.

'His name was Major Davenport and he was of the waxed moustache and leather gaiters variety, very much of the old school. I started by cleaning floors and so on and sometimes mixing the drugs. Drugs then were not drugs in our sense of the word. If you go into traditional chemist shops now you sometimes see the old drawers which they have kept as mementos of an earlier age, full of ancient drugs like nux vomica and ginger and aromatic powders and oils. That was the kind of pharmacopia we had in those days between the wars.

'It was the boy's job, under direction, to mix the odd gramme or two of this with the odd gramme or two of that, or to take this liquid and add a colouring agent to it so that, from the "brown drench", it became the "black drench" or the "pink drink". And that was the veterinary surgeon's armoury. People nowadays say that most of it was useless but that is unfair. Nux vomica, for example, was strychnine-based and formed a good stimulant; and if you were treating an animal that needed stimulants, it would work.

'The Major was frightening to work for and I was in absolute terror of him. He was very military; he expected even the animals to obey *on the instant*. He'd shout at them and he'd shout at me, too, in the days when performing castrations meant I had to run for hot irons and verdigris and clamps. We didn't use anaesthetics – well, perhaps local ones, or very occasionally chloroform. Instead it was all done with ropes: you just cast the animal and got on with it.

'He would drive into the farm and expect the colt to be standing there ready on his arrival, with plenty of farmhands holding it. If they were not there and at attention, he would roar off out of the yard in his car and say that he'd come back next week and they'd better be sure they were ready for him.'

By 1945, when his schooldays were nearing their end, Bob announced that he wanted to go into the veterinary profession. The war conveniently ended just as he was due to be called up but then the government decided that everybody must do their National Service before going to college. So Bob found himself in the army for the next two-and-a-half years. When asked what arm of the army he would like to go into, he naturally suggested the Royal Army Veterinary Corps.

'They said, "There isn't one." I said, very daringly at age seventeen and a bit, "Yes, sir, I'm sorry, sir, but there is. I'm sure there is, sir." "There isn't," they said. "You can have the Tank Regiment or Royal Artillery." I didn't mind which. "Royal Artillery," I said. So they posted me to the Parachute Regiment. Later they sent me to Palestine for the rest of my army career, attached to a Royal Artillery regiment just outside Haifa.'

He entered the Royal Veterinary College in London in 1948 and qualified in 1955. Then he returned to the Christchurch practice. As a newly qualified veterinary surgeon, he had something of a baptism of fire.

'The very first calving I ever had to do on my own was Siamese calves: two full-size calves joined back to back. It's the only one I have ever seen, and it just would be my first calving, wouldn't it? Now in those days you did embryotomy: if you couldn't calve them, you cut up the dead calf inside the cow to save the cow. We had these two great barbarous tubes welded together, about four foot long. You threaded a cheesewire up through it, into a loop, and back down the other one, and on the end of them you had two handles. You would feed this into the cow's uterus and you would take the wire up and try to put it round something. You'd try to lodge the wire round the calf's shoulder and then saw it off to remove a leg. Or ideally, if the calf's hips were jammed so it was coming out back legs but the hips stuck, you would try and get your hand in and use a special knife that fitted on your finger to make a hole; then you would pass the wire over the top and out, and saw the pelvis in half so the pelvis would collapse and you could get the calf out. Extremely hard work, all gristle.

'Embryotomy was your first line; one didn't usually do caesareans. Anyway, with this calving I couldn't make it out; it's not the sort of thing anybody tells you about at college. I was constantly trying to push one calf back in order to produce the other, but when I pushed one calf the other would also go back. I'd no idea they were joined. I spent hours trying to sever bits off.

'At five in the morning I finally finished. I'd had to do a caesarean. The calves were dead, of course, and we had to shoot the mother. The whole thing was awful, but the farmer said, "Well done, young man, you did very well. Come in and have some breakfast together." And it was the first time I've come across anyone who eats uncut macaroni for breakfast. I just sat at the table and heaved – it looked exactly like intestines.

'I learned a lot from that episode, and not just about difficult calvings: I discovered something about human nature. The farmer and I became great friends after our shared experience and we got on like a house on fire. You often find that in the veterinary profession: it's the failures that made you friends, not the successes. If you succeed with a case, then that's routine. But if you fail, and fail well and nicely, then that's good!'

Like most of his group, Bob had come out of college with the fixed intention of getting into a country practice as quickly as possible, to try and earn some money after several years at veterinary college. 'You wanted to *practise your art*, I think, more than the money. You really wanted to work and utilise some of the knowledge they had taught you.'

On the day he got his degree, he had become engaged to marry Anne. With marriage on the horizon, he needed a job that offered him an adequate salary. He took one at Dulverton in December 1955 for £10 a week.

'At Dulverton I remember being called to a whelping in a house in the woods up the Exe valley, on the Rothwell estates. I think he probably worked as a woodsman and they gave him a house in the woods with no electricity. She bred dogs. If anybody breeds dogs, you really don't want to know – you should go the other way and forget the whole thing. As I drove up this long, dark, wooded drive, the whole house *barked* – the house seemed to move with barking dogs; they were at every port-hole.

'Well, I went up the path with my little case, all keen and new, and knocked at the door. A woman opened it, only about thirty-five years old. "You the vet?" "Yes." She said, "I'm afraid there's only one room." I said, "I don't need more than one room to whelp a bitch." And we started to go upstairs with an ancient oil lamp. We went upstairs and she says, "Now, my dear, I think it would be better if you turned round and went backwards."

So I turned round and went backwards – and promptly sat on the loo! That was the one room, the room of which she spoke. So I said, "Okay." She said, "You stay there, my dear, and I'll go and get the dog." And she left me sitting on the loo in the dark.

'She came back with a little whippet bitch who was obviously in dire distress and with the oil lamp. I couldn't quite see what I was doing, and I said so. Well, the problem with oil lamps was that if you wanted a little bit more light, you automatically turned the wick up. And all that usually happens then is that the thing oils up massively, pouring unburnt oil out from the top. Well, everything got darker, not lighter, but we carried on and whelped the bitch; we got this puppy out that had been badly stuck crossways. And then we discovered that we were all drenched with soot – it was in our hair and clothes and everywhere. The wretched lamp had really smoked.'

Bob had many experiences in the Dulverton practice, some of them alarming, some sad and some thoroughly uncomfortable: 'The first cow I ever calved on Exmoor, the cow was actually trying to produce the calf with her backside laid in the River Barle. So I had to get in there and help. It was in the middle of winter and I had to strip off and get into the water.

The Dulverton practice was entirely large animals. It was hard work and very good experience for a young veterinarian. But the pay didn't increase and whenever Bob asked for time off he was told: 'We don't do that. Oh no, no. You can have an evening off next month ...' It was hardly ideal for newly-weds, but they stayed for nearly two years. Then Bob answered an advertisement to work with a veterinary surgeon in Corby. The salary was better and there was a nice new bungalow in the middle of Corby, in its only private road; the surgery was a wooden shed in the back garden.

Corby was a huge steel town and they did have their doubts about living there; he was really very happy in the South-West. However, he found himself under pressure from the practice to accept, and being a man who does not like to say no, he eventually agreed to join them.

'It was a funny practice. The boss told me how it worked. "I shall phone you up every morning, give you a list of jobs; then I phone again in the evening and you tell me exactly what you did." One of the partners lived in Uppingham, one lived in Market Harborough, one in Corby and he would ring them all up, giving them their orders, telling them where to go. In other words, all the calls came through him and he spread them out. Well, that was all right. It wasn't the way we worked, but it was all right.

'So I said, "Okay, if that's the way you want it. Where are the drugs?" I hadn't seen any sign of any drugs at Corby. He said, "Your drugs are all in the garage." We went into the garage and there were these carboys, big containers holding about twenty-five litres of different coloured fluids – browns, greens, pinks and blues. "Those are your drugs," he said. And I thought, good heavens, this is going back to the pre-war days of brown drench, green drench and red drench. Then he added to the insult by saying, "You give that one on the first day, that one on the second day and that one on the third day. As you are the third assistant, you will probably use up most of *that* one."

'It didn't make any sense. He could have been talking Chinese! I said, "Hang on, sir, is it irrespective of what I am treating?" "Quite irrespective," he said. "Don't you worry about what the diagnosis is; you use *that* one, you will be on the third day." What was all this third day business? He said, "We visit all patients three days running. Because you are the third one down the line, you go on that day and give them that drench."

'Well, I suppose there were a few bottles of calcium for milk fever floating around but that was all. Penicillin prices were still a bit beyond the veterinary scope and he said, "If you want penicillin, you come and get it from me, and I will let you have one dose." But he lived fifteen miles away. "You will draw it from me. I do not let any outside my sight until you give me a full account of what it is you are going to use it on." I couldn't believe it.'

Bob only stayed with the Corby practice for ten months, the same term as his hapless predecessor. Despite the nice house and the friends they had made in the town, he was longing to get back to Devon.

'I couldn't wait – I absolutely *itched* to be back here. So we looked at two or three jobs down south and I accepted one in Torrington. It turned out to be *very* hard work: tuberculin testing was becoming compulsory then and there were hundreds of herds to be tested for the first time. The farmers were totally ill equipped and unready, and not only that, they were also dead belligerent against it anyway: they didn't see why they should have to get their cattle in and they were not in the least co-operative. The conditions were often very poor and you'd be trying to test a hundred cattle between gates and in awkward situations. One day I went to a farm outside Beaford. The farmhouse was a shambles and the only way they could do it was to feed the cattle round the back of the farmhouse and then get them to jump in through the derelict window of the kitchen. So in they jumped, cantered past the stove and out through the back door. And you tried to take their numbers and jab them with the needle before they literally battered their way out of the kitchen. They were totally wild, these beef herds – Hereford crosses and a lot of Ruby Reds, North Devons, nice cattle. Great fun but very hard work, and a shortage of time off: about one weekend in four on average. Which was an improvement!

'By now I was in my thirties and wondering about a partnership, but he wouldn't give me one at Torrington. So we were on the move again. It was 1960 and I came here first as an assistant, then I bought half of it, then I bought another small practice in the locality, and eventually it turned into quite a reasonable size for a country practice. I did mostly large animals, bringing in assistants after a few years. And then along came Herriot. His first book made a massive difference to the profession, and all at once small animal practice really took off.'

He has few regrets about his career. 'It is the best thing I ever did. My parents wanted me to be a solicitor or a banker, but if you are a real sceptic, like me, you know that this is the best job because it is such hard work. And hard work in this life is the easiest way to go through it, because if you work hard you don't have time to think. You don't ever have to wonder what to do, or what is the best thing to do at this moment: shall I paint a picture, or write a book, or whatever. If you think, you don't do it. But if you're working hard, you just do it, on the instant, you don't stop to wonder. To my mind, a profession like this is the laziest way to go through life. And the easiest way out has always been my ideal.'

Laziness seems a strange word for Bob to apply to himself. We go for a stroll on Dartmoor, at the double as if he were still in the Greenjackets, haring up the tors and pausing only briefly to admire the far-reaching views above Headland Warren Farm, leaping from rock to rock over the streams, marching up ancient stone pathways and around stone pounds, ignored by little groups of cattle, sheep and ponies that roam freely over the moor.

In retirement Bob keeps busy, serving his local community on a voluntary basis in countless ways. He helps in the Citizens' Advice Bureau; he drives old folks in a minibus on various outings; he goes to a local school and creates little plays with the children. This man is so full of enthusiasms and so adept at self-mockery, so easy to talk with – and yet, underneath, he is still the shy young vet who never liked to say 'no' to anybody.

THE SHEEP OF THE ISLES

ooooo

The River Clyde rises in Scotland's protective southern uplands and finds its way down to the broad vales and plains that lie between the great cities of Glasgow and Edinburgh. From Tinto Hill, rising above this central Scottish plateau, it used to be possible to see eight counties; today you can only see three local government 'regions'.

The river's route beyond the Tinto hills takes it by the old stonebuilt town of Lanark. A little way upstream is New Lanark, a working settlement created in the late eighteenth century by David Dale, who recognised that the waters of the Clyde and the damp local atmosphere here offered the perfect setting for water-driven cotton mills. Dale's village for his workers was a socialist Utopia. He was succeeded as mill owner by another benevolent capitalist and free thinker, the Welshman Robert Owen.

If you follow the winding, rising and falling lanes from Lanark, where not so long ago the horses laboriously drew carts uphill and then struggled to control them on the descent, you come to the site of Robert Owen's house, Braxfield, into which he moved in 1800. This great stone edifice is now a ruin, quite hidden in the embrace of rampant ivy and brambles, its tall windows empty, its walls stretching to the rafters uninterrupted by any ceilings, its huge fireplace bare of embers.

The once extensive lawns, that the oldest of the locals can

remember as the site of summer fêtes, have long since been afforested with conifers. The old walled garden, nestling in a sheltered little valley of its own, is a neglected haven where a young fox suns itself undisturbed and thinks idly about catching a few mice in the undergrowth. A moorit (brown) Shetland ram nibbles peacefully nearby.

The small estate is a pleasant mixture of gentle hills, pasture and woodland. The parkland, where Owen planted lime trees and where a palomino mare now grazes, is gradually being restored, and the walled garden soon will be, by retired veterinary surgeon Marshall Watson, who lives in a one-storey stone home up the hill from the ruin. There is an old stone dairy in the paddock, and a fine stone stable block near the house, its woodwork painted oxblood red and the stone (which in Lanark itself looks severe) mellowed by hanging baskets of flowers. The house is a welcoming one, as are its owners: Norma's homemade scones are still warm from the oven and indescribably delicious.

James Marshall Watson, always known as Marshall greets me, jokingly, in incomprehensible Icelandic: he has just returned from a week or two in Iceland, a land that holds a particular fascination for a man so interested in primitive breeds of sheep such as the Hebridean and the Shetland. He is dressed in a tweedy brown jumper that might have come straight off the backs of a moorit flock. He stands some six feet tall, with dark brown hair, and has an affably rugged air about him.

Marshall bought Braxfield in 1967, ten years after he began practising in Lanark. He was born in 1928, quite out of context in Southampton: his father was by then a chief marine superintendent with the Union Castle shipping line at Southampton, though both sides of the family were from Strathaven (not far from Lanark). In 1936 Marshall's father died, only in his forties, and the family returned to Strathaven, where Marshall's mother's relatives still farmed. The small boy quickly became interested in livestock: he was taught to milk cows by hand and to hold Border Leicester ram lambs at shows and sales for his uncle.

'And then one day at school, a boy whispered along the row of seats: would I like a rabbit? I thought I had better ask my mother before I said yes. Well, she said "No", but my uncle said, "Yes, he's getting a rabbit; if he wants a rabbit, give the laddie a rabbit." I worshipped this rabbit. I watched it for hours and a wonderful new world opened for me. These animals were ... they were not little people but they were separate living things, they were real life. Far better than toys you wound up. This intrigued me. And so I got another rabbit and started breeding Dutch rabbits. Then I wanted something that bred faster than rabbits and so I got some mice, and that led into a fascination with colour genetics. I read books, I read *Fur and Feather*, I took my animals to shows. And I was always fascinated by the way different colours arrived when you put various colours of parents together.

'Then it became a bit commercial: I saw an advert in *Fur and Feather* from the Yorkshire Hospital Board wanting 21-day-old female mice. So for several of my teenage years I would (in the days when the railways carried livestock) put my 21-day-old coloured and white mice on the train for Bradford. I got a shilling each for them.'

Marshall's intention was to enter veterinary college on leaving school, but that proved impossible at the time, due to the priority being given to ex-servicemen. He therefore joined the army in 1946. Naturally he wanted to join the Veterinary Corps, but this was reserved for officers and so they put him in the Ordnance Corps for two years. To what exotic places did he travel in his army career? 'I was only abroad at night. They actually sent me to Glasgow!' At last he was accepted by Glasgow's veterinary college and he qualified from there in 1953.

His first job in practice was at Lochgilphead, but not for long: he saw an advertisement for a job in Jersey, where his brother had a chemist's shop. 'I love Jersey. And I love the Jersey cattle. I found that they were especially valued by their owners, so there was a great rapport between me, the animal lover, and the farmers. Later, when I returned to practice on the mainland, it was quite a cultural shock to find how commercial people could be about animal life. But perhaps that was just part of the maturing process.'

After less than a year on Jersey, Marshall felt he needed more experience and he took an appointment in Leicestershire.

'They were very decent people, one a Scot and the other the next best thing, a local lad. They didn't treat me as a new boy, other than to hand me a map and point out where I was supposed to be going. I was allowed to make my own decisions and there was a freedom of action that made me realise that, at last, I was no longer an apprentice. I was a journeyman.'

With an impending marriage and a lack of housing in the area, he reluctantly left Leicestershire and went to a job in Cupar, Fife, where a house was available. Here he remained for two very happy years until he chanced to see an advertisement in the *Veterinary Record* for an assistant, with a view to partnership, in Lanark, the homeland of both himself and his wife. So they went home.

Over the years Marshall built up a four-vet practice in Lanark, Carluke and Motherwell and Wishaw. But there was something else in the background, an interest which would lead him into different fields. It all began with Jacob sheep in the late 1960s and his interest in them encouraged a wider interest in the conservation of rare breeds of livestock, a subject about which he is passionate.

He had bought ten ewe lambs and a tup lamb soon after first becoming aware of these unusual piebald, four-horned parkland sheep. He began to win prizes with his flock, but this soon bored him: Jacobs were getting increasingly popular in the show-ring and people were beginning to breed them into 'woolly poodles – the powderpuff mentality'. With his sound background in agriculture and the veterinary sciences, not forgetting his youthful experiments in the genetics of colour inheritance, he did not think that showing and breed conservation went well together. The practicality of the breed was being lost in favour of looks.

He became aware that other interesting older breeds had become rare and were in danger of extinction. 'I knew about gene banks for flowers and vegetables and apples and so on, and I thought there should be something similar for breeds of farm animals. The aim would be to monitor the breeds and carry out serious research into why they had existed originally and what their genetic qualities were: the biochemical side of it, and qualities such as hardiness and thriftiness, rather than fancy points like ear carriage and colour.'

In the early 1970s, Marshall was judging Jacob sheep at the Flint and Denbighshire Show when he discovered that other people had similar ideas on breed conservation. He came across a little stand promoting the survival of rare breeds and was impressed by their arguments. He soon became involved with the new Rare Breeds Survival Trust and was persuaded to be one of two office-bearers for the Scottish arm of the Trust.

Marshall gradually became more and more involved in the work of the Trust and it gave him a splendid excuse to become familiar with the Scottish Isles, especially the Orkneys and Shetlands. His interest in Jacobs naturally extended to the island sheep and he soon found himself visiting the Trust's first major project on the little island of Linga Holm, where they established a flock of the remarkable seaweed-eating North Ronaldsay sheep in what was in effect a feral situation.

'I went up to Linga Holm several times. The little airplane lands on a cowfield on Stronsay nearby – the owner knows in advance to move the cows out but the splatter of cow dung as the plane touches down is a reminder of how slender are the trappings of civilisation! We used to go up for a week or so at a time to round up the sheep, check them over for any problems and select the culls. Marvellous days.'

The Orkneys made many impressions on Marshall Watson. 'The birdlife is tremendous, and the seal life. I felt that mankind was *not* in control, that we were only part of the environment and were not pulling the strings. It does make you a bit more humble: it isn't we who change the world, we are changed by the world. It's so beautiful there. And Kirkwall and the villages we visited always seemed so clean, free from rubbish and graffiti – well, the rubbish was removed by the wind and rain! It was one of the few places where you never had to lock the door when you left home and it is perhaps Scotland as it used to be. The islanders might protest that they are not Scottish, but much of their character reflects the Scotland of yesterday.'

In about 1980, the Rare Breeds Survival Trust heard that the last two good herds of native cattle in the Shetlands were to be dispersed and Marshall was sent to the islands to evaluate the situation and trace such Shetland cattle as remained there. He already knew the area well from his interest in Shetland sheep and he had some idea of what the traditional type of Shetland cattle should look like.

'In my boyhood, cattle dealers in my area would buy in cattle from the Shetland Islands, bringing them down as feeders, and sometimes the small ones would be pointed out to me and I would be told that those were the real Shetland cattle. I liked the pretty looks of the real Shetlands.

'Anyway, I went up and talked to the Shetland cattle breed

society and went through their pedigree records, then visited outlying crofts to identify and authenticate existing cattle. I found that the old crofters' cows were all being crossed with Hereford bulls – and that meant that the cycle was broken. The original Shetland cow was a crofter's cow: they were hand-milked and tame, though they are reputedly difficult to handle except by their owners. But by crossing with Hereford you turned the housecow into a suckler cow rearing a beef calf and she becomes much wilder because she's not being handled every day. And then if you do decide to have a purebred Shetland calf from her, you have broken the cycle: she is no longer your tame handmilker, you've lost that temperament. The calf will not be tame either, unless you hand-rear it with bucket feeding so that it will look forward to each visit by its owner with a pail of warm milk.

'I was still finding the occasional little old lady who still hand-milked her Shetland cow and was only too pleased to see me, but she was wondering where she would get her next Shetland calf. People thought that Hereford beef crosses were far more economic, but others understood that the Shetland cow was a link with the past which fitted with the layout of the farm, it was the cow they had grown up with; they understood them and how to feed them in an area where the growth period of fresh grass is short, and the weather usually too wet to make hay. The Shetland cow is adapted to that environment and can be fed frugally on what they can grow there.

'When I looked at the 1926 Shetland cattle herd book I found a whole range of colours listed: white with black ears, red-and-white, black with a white ridge on the back, blue-and-white, roans, reds, yellows and so on. Intriguingly, those colours are all still found today but not in the Shetland cows, which are now always black and white. They are in Icelandic cattle. And I'm sure they are related. My theory is that the Vikings brought their cattle with them when they came from Norway; they occupied Orkney and Shetland and colonies around York, Dublin, the Scottish west coast (where Ayrshire cattle came from), all the north of Scotland. Then the colonies collapsed. When I went to Iceland recently I found in Reykjavik that at that stage the island of Iceland was divided into forty family seats, twenty-seven of which were for families directly from Norway and the rest for Viking families from Orkney and Shetland and the collapsed colonies. When they went to sea, they took with them their cattle and sheep and ponies, and also their cats, and stowaway mice in the hay – which accounts for the genetic similarities between the Icelandic mice and cats and those from Scotland and Norway.

'And then, just imagine: Eric the Red, they say, went to America, and the cats and mice of the eastern seaboard of the United States have the same genetic make-up as Icelandic ones.

'Icelandic cattle, until *very* recently, have never interbred with other cattle. The dairy herds are virtually unchanged from those of the Viking days, except their milk yields have been greatly increased. But they have grown in size and I wouldn't like to take any of today's cattle in a longboat! Though they could have taken calves. The conformation of the Icelandic cattle is very similar to the traditional Shetland, very dainty.

'It's the same with the Orkney and Shetland sheep. No doubt the Shetland sheep have been improved out of all recognition from the time when the Vikings farmed them in the islands, but I don't think the Orkney sheep (which is exemplified in the North Ronaldsay) has changed all that far from its original ancestor. And the Icelandic sheep were taken from Orkney and Shetland. We know there was no outside material into Iceland after the Vikings and I often think, when I look into the face of a North Ronaldsay on Linga Holm, that these are the same eyes and the same face that a Viking looked into a thousand years ago: those bright, alert yellow eyes with a semi-wild gleam in them, and that sort of love/hate aura, that mixture of fear and affection, which is typical of an animal that lives on the edge of domestication.'

His imagination has clearly been fired by his visit to Iceland, and had been long before that visit. He recalls a moment at Linga Holm: 'We went over to stay in the farmhouse on Stronsay. Next morning, the fishing boat arrived to take off the cull sheep from the islands, for sale. As this red-sailed lugger grounded on the shore, I saw a large, red-bearded man standing like a Viking figurehead in the bows, gazing steadfastly into the distance with some Nordic twilight in his eyes. The landing was one his Viking ancestors must have done over the centuries.

'I asked who this fine figure was. "Oh," they said, "he's the village drunk; he sleeps in the phone box and if you want to make a call you have to wake him up and throw him out!" So another romantic dream was shattered: he was a down-and-out who looked good when he was sober.'

Watson is pleased that he managed to buy half a dozen true Shetland cattle and a bull calf for the Trust and shipped them to the mainland to be reared by Joe Henson and other members. 'With this small nucleus, I felt I had done a little something to ensure the future of the breed.'

Dealing with Shetland cattle made Marshall realise that he wanted to be involved in conservation for the rest of his life: it had become more important to him than veterinary work. He parted company with his own veterinary practice in 1982.

It is fitting that a Watson should have taken a hand in saving rare breeds: Marshall's great-great-grandfather was the Victorian artist Horatio McCulloch, who painted landscapes of Glasgow and Edinburgh and also of the Duke of Hamilton's estate. Many of his paintings of that estate featured White Park cattle in

Cadzow Forest in the nineteenth century, and the White Park is the symbol of the Rare Breeds Survival Trust.

For many years Marshall Watson bred horses: show ponies, Thoroughbreds, riding ponies and especially palominos, which are something of a rarity in the UK, though very popular across the Atlantic: 'I have only one now, that cream mare in the field. She's had three lovely palomino foals, including two by the son of Aureole (the Queen's Derby winner) that we sold as a matched driving pair, matching full brother and sister.

'Of course the local breed of horse is the Clydesdale, but it's a minority one now and nobody works them round here any more. They are kept as fancy show things – you know, like dahlias. Everybody breeds towards big heavy bones and they're becoming over-white, a lot of white markings extending up the legs and the body colour is lightening to a roan. A lot of hunters are based on Clydesdales and Shires, perhaps a quarter of one or the other for the big size and heavy bone, the rest Thoroughbred.'

Gradually Marshall realised that there could not be a 'serious career' for him in the Rare Breeds Survival Trust, though he remained passionate about conservation. He did not return to practice, but settled for local government as his employer, more as an expedient than because it was what he wanted. He ultimately became Edinburgh's 'city vet', its Chief Veterinary Officer. His duties were concerned with licensing and hygiene standards in dog boarding and breeding kennels, riding schools, pet shops and so on, and he also kept an eye on Edinburgh Zoo. Above all, he had to be qualified as a meat hygienist, in which role he travelled daily to Edinburgh, rising at 4.30 in the morning in order to ensure the maintenance of high standards in slaughterhouses and meat plants.

Such a role might seem strange for a man who has spent his life keeping animals alive and well, and conserving endangered breeds, but it does make sense. His veterinary training has given him a sound knowledge of bacteriology and anatomy on the one hand and a depth of compassion for animal welfare on the other, tempered with realism:

'It is a principle of mine that everything which militates towards the comfort of the animal prior to death is also important from the economic point of view. If I say to people, "Don't hit cattle with sticks", not only do I stop an infringement of the animal's welfare but I also save the meat from being bruised. If I say, "Don't lift sheep by the wool", I am also stopping the inevitable tearing of subcutaneous tissues and bruising. If I say, "Make sure the sheep have plenty of drinking water", it also means that they don't lose weight, nor do they become dehydrated, so the pelts come off much more easily, like peeling a ripe orange. If I say, "Don't play such loud music in the lairage", I know that if the animals are resting properly and are peacefully chewing the cud, then the meat is going to be of a natural colour when they are slaughtered. The same applies if I say, "Don't let a dog into the lairage", because it would upset and excite the bullocks.

'So I am still carrying out welfare, and everything I do for the welfare of the animals is also in the interests of the trade. That is a strong argument to use when you are dealing with people whose livelihood is involved.

'When you have spent your life saving animals, it's a huge cultural shock when you first come to a slaughterhouse. A lot of vets don't face up to the fact that they are responsible for the dead animal as well as the live animal. We all spend most of our lives attempting to postpone death, if not avoid it altogether. But this is the other side of the coin, and to think that there are rows of animals there that are all going to die, going to die, going to die – it takes some adjustment emotionally. But when you have achieved that and you get a grip on yourself and look at it logically, then you make a better job of it and you make certain that there's no infringement of the welfare regulations, which are there to protect the animal from pain and distress until it becomes unconscious. To slaughter an animal efficiently requires a respect for the animal in life in order to kill it.

'Although I'm in the slaughter business, I cannot understand those who take pleasure in killing animals. In particular I can't understand people who go out and shoot birds, and even breed the birds in order that they can be shot "for fun". To take a gun and then spend the afternoon mortally wounding birds and animals – that's against all my principles.

He returns to the subject of humanely taking the life of an animal, which is inevitably part of the work of any veterinary surgeon. 'I was once asked to put down a Pekingese and the chap said, "I'll put you in here". Well, "here" was a disused coal-shed without any windows. So there I was in the dark, with this snarling Peke in my hand; I managed to get it by the scruff of the neck, and then pushed the needle in. And then I felt a tremendous pain in my finger: I must have stabbed myself with the needle. I staggered to the door – and found that in fact the dog had its teeth through my nail. But until that moment I wasn't sure which one of us was going to die first.'

He laughs ruefully, but he has many serious points to make about the relationship between humans and animals: 'You find now that so many farmers are removed from close contact with their animals, which have become just units of production for meat, milk and money. I think there should be a basic test or even a licence before you are allowed to own livestock. We have domesticated these species and removed them from their natural environment; we have changed them to adapt to our lives and to the environment that suits *us* so that they now rely on us.

We have a historical and moral obligation to look after them.

'It's the same with veterinary surgeons: we are part of the agricultural industry, after all, and we should be aware of the responsibilities that we take on ourselves when a species is domesticated. Furthermore a vet needs to understand animals but he also needs to understand the owner, especially the relationship of owners with companion animals like dogs and cats. We are not just animal vets, we are *community* vets: animals have a role for people. They mean so much to the elderly and the lonely, and are the fun for, say, a miner with a racing dog or a terrier for rabbits; animals are a part of people's lives.'

In his retirement, Marshall Watson has several aims. 'I am going to breed the perfect moorit Shetland ram and use it to breed a flock of animals of the highest quality. And I want to maintain a flock of the many-faceted Hebridean sheep: I would want the type as a lean, hard animal that can stand the Hebridean winter in a force ten gale with the shell sand of the machair whistling about its ears and blowing about on the exposed Atlantic beaches in mid-February. I would like to round off my life in some way, doing these two things and trying to keep my interest in the world that I have known.'

He falls into a philosophical frame of mind. 'You know, we are all animals under the skin and we should look at animal behaviour to understand human problems. We really haven't evolved that far, have we? And even the most sophisticated city-dweller is only a few generations away from the soil. Even those who think that they want a house with no garden and don't want even a budgie, let alone a dog – they still go for drives in the country, they still decorate the house with flowers. Aware of it or not, they still have an interest in the natural world, the real world out here. It's just that they haven't had the good fortune to live in it. And I have!'

LUCKY JIM IN THE COTSWOLDS

ooooo

A blue haze of flax fills the fields, magically disappearing for part of the day and then returning to surprise you with its wash of colour. Scarlet poppy swathes sweep through the cornfields here and there and the uncut road verges are rampant with other wildflowers in soft mauves and bright yellows. The landscape is one of gentle hills and broad vales, dotted with mellow golden stone villages and farms. This is the English jewel: summer in the Cotswolds.

It is dawn, between four and five in the morning. Foxes slide across the lanes ignoring lone humans at an hour that belongs to the wildlife. Flocks of pigeons and a few crows peck in the grit of the road, taking advantage of this empty time before the vehicles claim it as their own. Down in the vales the cows are calling each other up for milking, some of them plaintively shouting for a bull in voices that carry far in the stillness of the morning.

Around the town of Stow-in-the-Wold, the lanes spread out towards local hamlets and become increasingly narrow and apparently aimless. It is an area that is unnervingly short of signposts. No doubt many a new country vet has been lost in these lanes, searching for unnamed farms hidden in the folds of the hills. Fortunately the route to Hunters Spinney has been carefully described. The extensive gardens are immaculately kept and beautifully stocked, drawing the eye to a wholly rural view across the fields to a distant, tiny stone village.

John Penfold is a faintly Celtic man with thick short black eyebrows, a stiff limp, and a vague air of suppressed anger. He has reason to be angry: his career as a veterinary surgeon was cut short far too early, when in November 1991 his car was smashed into by a continental bus whose driver had forgotten that he was on this side of the channel, where the natives have the odd habit of driving on the left-hand side of the road. As a result, John ended up with a foot injury so bad that the doctors told him he would never walk on that foot again. By determination and courage and with a great deal of support from family and friends, he proved them wrong, after a year in plaster; but he has not been agile enough since the accident to practise again. He has recently trained to work as a veterinary arbitrator, and continues his involvement with several veterinary societies devoted to unusual species such as deer and llamas. He also finds himself in demand as a speaker for local organisations; he has a natural flair for telling good stories.

John was born in 1942 in Hertfordshire but his father, a cabinet-maker, was originally a Sussex man. When the boy was about thirteen or fourteen, his father introduced him to a long-standing family friend, Bill Widdicombe, a dairy farmer with a large herd of Ayrshires at Ditchling, beneath and on the Sussex downs. 'He wants to be a vet,' his father told Widdicombe. 'Would you confirm or refute his feeling and take it from there?'

And so John began to spend his holidays on the farm, taking the train to Sussex on the day school broke up. 'Widdicombe taught me really how to conduct myself. He taught me a tremendous amount. If he was showing, I went to the show with him; I was introduced to young farmers, I entered the Ayrshire Club judging competitions. He taught me not only what I already knew, that I wanted to be a vet, but also – much more valuable to me – he taught me things from a *farmer's* angle.'

The farm was quite large: they were milking 200 Ayrshires and had a pedigree Wessex Saddleback herd of pigs as well. Much of the land was up on Ditchling Beacon, most of it down to barley on scrubland that had been cleaned up by the pigs. The men would bring the harvest 'all the way down the hill to Court Gardens Farm in the days when tractors had no brakes'.

'My job in those days was to bucket-feed the calves at five in the morning, and to give the youngstock their concentrates and forage in the winter. After breakfast it was mucking out the pigs. I didn't do a lot of milking to start with as I wasn't strong enough. They had a very modern abreast parlour with twelve standings and it took three hours to milk the herd. All the milk went into churns which had to be individually cooled with rotating inserts and then transferred to the loading platform by the dairy for collection by lorry.

'In the harvest field my job in the first few years was to ride the homemade sledge. This thing comprised two heavy great sheets of corrugated iron, with a bar joining the two across the front, leaving a two-inch gap down the middle. I would stand on the front, building piles of bales on the two sheets: the first two bales across the sledge, the next two at right-angles and so on to a stack four or five high. When I had enough bales in the pile, I would grab a crowbar and stick it between the two iron sheets, stabbing it into the ground to stop the bales moving and jump off while the sledge carried on ahead. Then I had to yank out the bar and run after the thing to jump on again while it was still moving and catch the next lot of bales as they left the baler. It was very stony up on the Beacon, the ground covered with bloody great flints that frequently tipped the sledge over. And of course the tractor driver sometimes had a bit of fun with me by accelerating – you can imagine ...'

John loved his working holidays on the farm but realised there was no hope of becoming a farmer himself: that would need capital. But he was more than content to follow his original dream of becoming a veterinary surgeon, and he entered college in London, qualifying in 1965. During his second or third year at London he went to attend his grandmother's funeral in Chepstow, Monmouthshire, and was chatting to a local vet, Ken Morgan.

'Ken was a marvellous man; I saw practice with him for about three years. He had his own herd of cows and I would milk them on the herdsman's day off, and I would dehorn the calves for him. He had qualified just before the war and ran a practice single-handed in Southampton in the days when the place was full of draft horses working for the breweries and the docks. There was a theory that the beer was essential for troops' morale and so Ken was excluded from military service in order to keep the horses fit! There weren't many lorries about at that stage – they'd all been taken abroad for the war–and so people pulled old carts out of sheds and got the horses working again.

'Ken was slightly built; he wore horn-rimmed glasses and had a trim moustache; he was a stickler for personal hygiene, and he was always tidily dressed, in a thornproof jacket with a red-and-white spotted handkerchief sticking out of its pocket. He had this very cultured voice if he was talking to the aristocracy or to old ladies, but he could cuss and swear with the best of them when necessary. He drove a Land Rover and always had a wire-haired fox terrier on the seat beside him.'

Morgan had an Irish assistant, Chris Jolley, as broad Irish as they come and a larger-than-life character with an enormous chest, very strong arms, a long straight back and thin little legs to support his bulk. Like Morgan, Chris would be impeccably dressed: he wore cavalry twills, a cream starched shirt and a tightly knotted tie with a gold pin crested with a horse's head under his thornproof jacket. His brown brogues always shone brilliantly. He rarely got himself into a messy situation in his work, but if he did, he would go straight home for a shower and a change of clothes.

Chris shared some interesting experiences: 'One very hot summer's day we had to do a TT test for Jack Williams at Trelleck Grange. Jack was blind, but he farmed a dairy herd with the help of his two sons – who took every advantage of his blindness (much to Chris's disgust). Anyway, come lunchtime and we were nowhere near finished with the job. Jack invited us in for bread and cheese and pickled onions, all washed down with pint glasses of an amber liquid; it went down well and we happily consumed a second pint. Then we rose from the table to continue our work – but Jack was the only one whose legs did what they were supposed to do! We had to abandon the test until the following day, during which Jack showed us the source of the amber liquid. He had a cider press in the yard, covered in dead flies and a dead rat and ... well!'

From college, John went to Lincolnshire for a year. Then he and his wife Kathy, a midwife, moved to Cranleigh in Surrey for a couple of years, where a caretaker and his wife lived over the premises. 'He was as thin as a knife, she like a plump cottage loaf.' John remembers being called out to Cranleigh School to attend to a swan that had flown into some wires and broken its wing. He brought it back to the surgery and the caretaker's wife took one look at it. 'Hmph,' she said, 'I know what to do with that.' She went into the yard, found a broomstick, put it across the swan's outstretched neck on the ground, stood her substantial weight on either end of the stick and pulled. It was a quick, clean death for a bird beyond saving. 'And it seemed a pity to waste it, so she plucked it and roasted it. Very dark meat but very good.'

John and Kathy were happy living in Cranleigh but the practice was somewhat old-fashioned and unwilling to change. So they began to look for more of a challenge and finally came to the Cotswolds to join the practice in Stow-on-the-Wold.

One of his many clients has been Joe Henson, joint proprietor of the nearby Cotswold Farm Park, one of the earliest and most famous centres for rare breeds of farm livestock in England: 'I first met Joe on a cold morning in November; his farm is an exposed one and it was wet and windy up there. He had a lot of calves in buildings round a yard beside the house and they were scouring like fury. It sounded like salmonella and I came along to check it out shortly after I had joined the practice. When I arrived the whole place was in turmoil. Someone showed me where the calves were; I did my assessment, took swabs and decided what needed to be done, then I was ushered into the kitchen to meet Joe. The place was full of folks in top hats and tails and women in hats: it was his brother's wedding day. Someone came up and said, "I'm Joe". I observed that it was obviously not the best moment to talk about scouring calves, and he agreed; so I came back on the Monday. He's a chip off the old block, is Joe, no airs and graces, and a great showman.

'I knew nothing about rare breeds then, and he had only a few at the time, in the early days. But I have grown with his collection; he has gradually added more over the years, and every time I went to test the herds there'd be something different to see. I had known that things like Longhorns and Highlands existed; I had seen Dexters; but I'd never heard of White Park cattle and those sorts of creatures.

'There was the day when I caesared his Gloucester, this young little heifer trying to calve, not a hope in hell, in a loosebox in the yard. So we did a caesar and it all went perfectly; we got a super live calf, everything was as it should be. It was early on a Monday morning and I had masses of work to do, so I stitched her up, saw that the calf was up and sucking as it should be and

I disappeared on my rounds, feeling well pleased. When I got back to the surgery, Joe had been on the phone: the cow had split her stitches and her guts were hanging out.

'It seems that the lad who had been helping us with the operation had thought the cow would like some fresh air after her ordeal and he'd opened the top half of the stable door. And the heifer had thought, yippee!, and tried to jump out. She landed smack on top of the half-door and everything burst. Her guts landed on the deck and she had trampled on them and ... well, we managed to hose it all off and stuff it all back in and stitch it up again, and she never looked back!'

Every vet has a parrot story and the Stow practice was no exception. 'There was a place called Birdland in Bourton-on-the-Water and they had a visitor with an old parrot, a lifelong family pet. The visitor's own vet wasn't in the least interested in the parrot and they asked Birdland for a recommendation. So the parrot arrived at Stow, accompanied by a very well spoken lady in a very well cut tweed suit and with very well groomed hair and carefully painted fingernails. She had an appointment with our senior partner, David Stewart, the Scotsman – he's the one who taught me to talk a lot!

'So he examined the parrot and it looked like a pregnant duck: it had a huge abdominal tumour. He and the client agreed on investigative surgery to see what should be done about the lump. She left the bird with him; he anaesthetised it, plucked the operation area, took out a tumour the size of a golf ball, put it all together again and laid it on the floor of its cage, covering the cage with a cloth until it came round properly. David checked it at intervals: gradually it came round; gradually it realised where it was; gradually it climbed on to its perch. When it seemed stable, they left it on the perch but still under the cover to keep it calm. David carried on with whatever he was doing, asking for it to be checked every ten minutes. Eventually there was an almighty shout; David raced over and found that the parrot on its perch had suddenly woken right up, realised that there was something different about its belly and had carefully undone it, stitch by stitch – its guts had landed on the floor of the cage and it had shrieked! David, in his broad Scots accent, called the bird every derogatory name you could think of, put it all together again and stitched it up – but this time gave it a little collar to stop it pecking at the stiches again.

'Well, it was discharged the following morning; the woman in tweeds came in and went off proudly with the bird. She returned a week later for a check-up and for the stitches to be removed. David took charge again. "How are things, Mrs ....?" "He seems to be fine," she said, "but there is one thing. He's talking. He has never said anything in all his life before, until this last week. And now he's saying all sorts of things, but I can't really understand what: it seems to be in a strong Scottish accent ..." Perhaps she was being tactful!'

It seems perhaps a little strange that a man who has devoted his working life to saving animals' lives has also relished the sport of deer-stalking, but John did indeed enjoy days out on the Scottish hills: in glorious scenery, spending hours flat on his stomach peering through binoculars as much as through the sights of his rifle. He has come to know a great deal about the veterinary care of deer and the art of handling these essentially wild animals without causing undue distress.

'Vetting has been a fantastic profession; it has given me so much. But it is a fairly hectic job, the stress can be huge and the suicide rate seems to be very high within the profession. And the job really is an abuse of your own body! One minute you will be picking up animals' feet, or heaving a calf out of a cow, doing something incredibly strenuous in one direction that needs a lot of strength; the next you are carrying out a delicate operation on a small animal in the surgery, or breaking the bad news to a client that their pet will have to be put down.

'I wonder if that part of it is something women handle better? Colleges now are half full with girls, which is a major change. London takes in about seventy-five a year, and of those forty will be women. There were only four girls out of the sixty in my year.'

Just as every vet has a parrot story, so too does every vet have a story about women. 'I must tell you about Sister Mater Die at the convent. They had a herd of cows there and a message came to me on a cold winter's night that a cow was in trouble calving; could I help? So I went over, and the place was in darkness, nobody around. I checked various buildings and eventually saw a dim light in one of them. In I went and there was Sister Mater Die, stripped to the waist and with her arm up the cow's backside dealing with the stuck calf. She'd completely forgotten they'd asked for help and was simply getting on with the job. She wasn't the least embarrassed – but I was!'

He cannot resist one last story. 'I was called out to a remote farm cottage about an injured cat. When I found it, I knocked at the door and nobody came, so I kept banging; it seemed to be dark inside. Eventually a man came to the door, ingrained with grime and dressed only in filthy Y-fronts. He let me in, gruffly. It was a very basic cottage indeed, no carpets, no furniture, no knick-knacks or anything. "Where's the cat?" I said. "What cat?" he grumbled. "Oh, it's in here, in the bedroom." He ushered me into this dim room with a bed in it – and on top of the bed there was a large mound. It moved: it was a huge woman, as grimy as he was and totally naked. 'Where's the cat?' I asked nervously. She pointed down to floor and then ignored me, rolling over in a leisurely fashion onto her stomach. All I remember is this mountainous pair of buttocks ... I took the cat and departed hastily.'

On the North Yorkshire Moors

ooooo

Tony Poole, an easy-going Yorkshireman who dresses informally but tidily, comes from a family that has lived around Pickering for possibly a thousand years. His father was a stationmaster with LNER and the family moved from station to station: they went from Pickering to Weaverthorpe, then to Grangetown near Middlesborough when Tony was eight, only to be bombed out and evacuated back to Pickering. A year later they were in Northumberland, not far from Morpeth.

'That was a farming and smallholding area and I soon finished up with four goats, a hundred rabbits, a couple of pigs and some hens. And you know, at that age (I was about ten) you learn a lot from literally keeping them. We were more or less self-sufficient during the war with milk, bacon and eggs, and garden produce: we used to make curds and butter and soft goat's cheese.

'I was always interested in the animals, how they worked. On the railway quite a lot of animals got knocked down – foxes, badgers, snakes, that sort of thing. The linesman knew I was interested and whenever he found something dead he'd hang it on the back door for me. I would spend my Saturdays after school dissecting badgers and foxes, skinning them and tanning the skins. I learned my anatomy that way! And if one of my rabbits died, I would always cut it up to see what had happened. I used to treat them myself, and if one had broken a leg or something my father would show me how to splint and bandage it.

'I don't know how he knew that; he was just one of those sort of people. He would have made a good vet himself, or a doctor: great sense of reassurance if you were ill, you know, and made you feel better immediately. And he was a very practical man. He'd worked on a farm in his youth and he taught me a lot about farming – how to use a scythe, how to harness a horse, make hay, stack the corn, all those little practical things that make an enormous difference when you're visiting a farm as a veterinary surgeon. He gave me a good background.

'One day, when I was about ten or eleven, my neighbour said, "I'm going to have someone put my old cat down. I don't want to have to hold it for them. Would you stick around?" Well, this vet came from a neighbouring practice; he grabbed this poor old cat and jabbed a great needle into it, shot in some cyanide. The cat went shrieking round the coalhouse – terrible, really, a most undignified performance, it wasn't the best that could be done by any means. And I thought, well, I could do better than that myself. And my father said, "Have you ever thought about being a veterinary surgeon?" That's what started the whole thing off.'

Tony continued his schooling, took his exams and eventually tried to enter one of the veterinary schools. But the war had just ended and National Service was looming. There was a choice: go to veterinary school immediately and do National Service after qualifying, or start with the National Service. He chose the latter and joined the Royal Army Veterinary Corps.

'I was posted to the first reserve veterinary hospital in Melton Mowbray, Leicestershire, where they had 600 horses and mules, and a dog section. That first winter of 1947 when I was in the army, it started snowing in November and went on until the spring. And you can imagine, we had 600 horses in the stables that winter and you couldn't get them out until April. The manure was stacked up like rows of houses. When we were on guard, we used to drag a horse blanket onto the big manure heaps and get on top to stay warm!'

Then he was posted to Porton Down, the chemical defence experimental station, and there he helped to look after cattle, horses, pigs, sheep, goats, rabbits, mice, rats and monkeys. The next move was a secret overseas operation taking monkeys, sheep and guinea pigs over to Antigua in the British West Indies.

'I was over there for nine months, which was very nice at His Majesty's expense. Never had a shirt on my back in all that time, except Sunday morning church parade!'

With his National Service completed, he came home and found that, with so many ex-servicemen flooding into the colleges, he had to wait a year before he could get a place. He moved back to Pickering and spent his waiting year working with the Forestry Commission in Thornton Dale forest. Then at last he started at Edinburgh's Royal Dick Veterinary College and was lucky enough be to given one of the further education and training grants that were available for those whose careers had been interrupted by their army service.

'It wasn't much. Was it £184 a year? We had to live on that: digs, food, books, clothing, travel, the whole works. When I went for interview and they asked what I'd been doing, I said I'd been in the Royal Army Veterinary Corps. "Oh good. Do you have any farming background?" I said, "Well, you know ..." The next question was, "Do you play rugby?" I said yes – at my school we hadn't been allowed even to *think* about soccer balls! "Oh good," they said, "what position? Oh, yes, fine, you'll get a place almost immediately." It counted for a lot, because our college fielded three rugby teams every Saturday.

'They were good times. A lot of hard work and there wasn't much free time, what with clinics and farm visits and visits to the zoo, and getting up at half past four in the morning to go to the slaughterhouse. There was a lot to cram in for the five years.

'I was nearly twenty-six when I qualified, and all I had in the world was a rucksack and a secondhand bicycle. In the Easter vacation we started to apply for posts, hoping we'd pass our finals in June. Two of us got a job at Hexham, in Northumberland, with Jock Pickering. Jock was a truly hardened old practitioner, an ideal man to start me off green from college; I can see him now, only a little man, standing with his thumbs in his braces.

'His was a very economically run practice. There was no money wasted on things like catgut: you boiled up lengths of linen or cotton thread. You sharpened your needles and used them again instead of throwing them away, like today.'

The medicines were typical of the time: 'Jock had a label which said, "Do not open this medicine within six feet of a naked flame!" printed in red. This was on a container of spirits of nitrous ether. If you took the cork off and happened to have a naked flame nearby, it would go off pop. Farmers used to love that.

'He had a bottle standing in the window coloured brown. I asked what it was for. He said, "When you make up a bottle of medicine, you stand it beside the sample bottle in the window and you put the brown caramel in to colour it so that it reaches the same colour, otherwise the farmer will say that it's paler, it's not as strong as the other medicine." He was right: they used to complain, "That young vet gave me this, it's light coloured, it isn't nearly so strong as yours." So all the senior men used to say, "Ah, yes, I'll put that right for you," and they'd put a bit more colouring matter in. It was coloured to a standard, you see.'

The Hexham practice was an extensive one, covering more than 2,000 square miles. 'I did 45,000 miles in my first year there, in a little Austin A30. The area of the practice wandered off into what is now Kielder Forest, it went over the Scottish border at Deadwater; it was forty-four miles to the furthest farm, along forest tracks and through fords. That was wild country then; the roads weren't made up as they are today. A lot of the farms we used to visit are under the reservoir now.

'My landlady, she was a nice old soul, she could never understand why I didn't eat very much. You'd get to a farm at ten o'clock in the morning and the farmer would say, "We're just going in for our ten o'clocks," and you'd go in and have a pot of tea, some homemade bread and a couple of slices of fat bacon. You'd get to your next farm about midday and the farmer would say, "We're just going in for our midday snack; come in, we're just going to have a bit of roast beef," and then you'd get somewhere in the afternoon and it would be, "Now, we're just having our afternoon tea," which was scones and jam and cold ham. Then my landlady would say, "Oh, you've been out for fifteen hours, out half the night, here's a nice dinner for you." Poor soul.'

Tony learned a lot with the Hexham practice but there was a problem. By that time his wife-to-be, Rhoda, a theatre staff nurse in Edinburgh, had come down to a hospital at Dilston, near Corbridge. They wanted to marry but Tony's boss was not inclined to buy somewhere for them to live.

'There were plenty of jobs going that offered married accommodation, so after a couple of years up in Northumberland I moved down to Market Rasen in Lincolnshire, to Glynn Beaumont's practice. He had been a colonel in the army, the Chindits, dealing with mules, devoicing them when they went behind the lines. I joined his practice as one of his two assistants, and Rhoda and I got married and had a flat above the surgery.'

At Market Rasen Tony spent a lot of his time dehorning cattle, TB testing, and vaccinating pigs against swine fever. There were some interesting characters about, too. He remembers a vicarage in Lincolnshire: 'It was a real Dickensian set-up. The vicar wore a cloak and a big, broad-rimmed hat. He rang up one winter's night, after dark. He had a bit of glebeland behind the church where he kept a few bullocks, and they had got into the churchyard, which of course was full of yew trees. I got over there fast. Some had already died from yew poisoning, others were sick and dying, groaning behind me in the pitch dark. And the vicar, who was about six foot four, was standing on top of one of the raised tombs with his big hat and wearing his cloak – he looked like Dracula himself! I was stumbling around through brambles and nettles trying to find these cattle in the dark to chase them out. We had to get in a tumbril the next day to drag out the ones that had already died.

'The house was a big, old-fashioned Victorian vicarage with a lot of rooms. He had two sisters who looked after him there but they had fallen out years ago. One of them kept cats and the other kept terriers. I used to go and see these cats and she was just like Miss Havisham in *David Copperfield*: she hadn't left her room for years and she used to wear pale pastel colours – lavender-coloured silk dresses, Edwardian ones. It was a huge room with built-in cupboards and an oak sideboard and all these kittens: the mother would have a nest of kittens inside one of these old cupboards where there were tumblers and glasses and crockery all thick with dust, and these kittens would have diarrhoea on one shelf running all over the stuff: oh, I can't describe the situation and the smell! And she used to say, "I must have something done with these kittens, Mr Poole, because, you see, I'm going on holiday next week; we're going to the Bahamas for a fortnight." But that was all in her head; she hadn't left that room for years.

'When I finished with her cats, she said, "Now, my sister wants to see you." I could hear these dogs yapping at the other side of the wall and I started to go to the door between the rooms. "Oh no," she said, "that door's nailed up." It was full of these big nails and you had to go out into the corridor, right round the vicarage and then round the other side. They hadn't spoken to each other for years; they just pushed notes under the nailed-up door.'

Ater three years Tony decided to head north again and his next post, with the prospect of a partnership, was a very busy dairy practice at Wigton in Cumberland.

'Wilson Clark was a very formal man. He'd had a very good record during the war; he flew Lancaster bombers. He was a good practitioner, a calm sort of man, very knowledgeable.'

Once again, Tony found himself dehorning cattle. He had done a great deal of dehorning in Northumberland; he had dehorned thousands of cattle at Market Rasen ('whole herds of Lincoln Red Shorthorns') and now his Cumberland boss said: 'There's a list on the wall there of clients who require cows dehorned. We fit them in when we can. There's about two thousand cows on that list that we've got to work our way through.' The prospect was a daunting one but the boss took his fair share of the work.

'He and I used to have a little bit of a competition between us. I went off one day and dehorned 116 cows – I don't think anybody had ever done more than sixty or seventy in a day before. So he went off next day and managed to do just two or three more. It was soul-destroying work, sawing horns off cattle, and you'd come back stiff with blood.'

After three years, although he thought it was a nice practice, he found that it was still 'Mr Poole' and 'Mr Clark' between them. He accepted that he had learned a lot but he began to think about moving on. Then, as chance would have it, he heard that Peter Fernie in Pickering was looking for an assistant. Of course Tony knew him of old: 'I was born in Pickering, my family had lived there for generations and I thought, well, it's always nice to be back in your own corner. So I came back here, thinking that it was a one-man practice which had never really been built up.'

Peter Fernie was well known on every northern race course – it was a good way of building up the practice. 'If you go to the races, know the trainers, know the horses, you're a betting man – then you get the horse trade. You know, when Fernie qualified in the 1930s, the horsey people wouldn't accept you if you had wellingtons with cow dung on them because that meant you were a cow doctor, not a horse doctor. And it got to a point in my own time when if you had a reputation as a dog and cat vet you were certainly considered to be no good for cattle.'

Two or three years after Tony joined the Pickering practice, Fernie developed cancer. For the next ten years or so, Tony was in effect doing the work of one and a half men. 'It was pretty hard work but physically I'm very lucky, I've never been ill apart from three days with 'flu once. He did his best, and we got on very well together. He was a quite remarkable man in his own way, a bit rough but he knew his stuff. It suited the times. Remember that when I started there was only penicillin and sulphur drugs, and as for anaesthetics, there was local anaesthetic and there was chloroform for large animals, and that was about it. Corticosteroids came in just after I qualified, which was useful, but otherwise we used to spend hours at night making up powders and drinks, fever drinks and cleansing drinks, to old-fashioned recipes in the books. Jock's people used to have whole sackfuls of sodium thiosulphate and sodium chlorate, African ginger, gentian powders, and liquid nux vomica with small amounts of strychnine.

'Human medicine wasn't much better at the time. You know, people think that doctors and vets are absolutely omniscient, and you're not. Like doctors, you're plunging your way through a whole range of unknowable things most of the time.'

He draws other parallels with doctors when he remembers the hours that he worked, especially during the year after Peter Fernie died. 'You hear the young doctors now saying that they work an eighty-hour week. I *always* worked an eighty-hour week – did nothing else for forty years. And when I was on my own after Peter's death I'd also be taking all the night calls and would be out at least once almost every night. It was a rare time during the week when I had one night without being called out, usually at 2 or 3am or 6am or something like that. I've worked forty-eight hours without even having time to take my clothes off, let alone sleep. The first three days after my partner died, I averaged 660 miles just driving in circles around here.'

After a year under such pressure, he found himself an assistant who in due course would become his partner. A few weeks after the new assistant had joined, Tony had his first weekend off in eleven years.

It was essentially a farm practice at that stage, of course, as were most of the rural practices at that time. 'Peter Fernie never was terribly keen on small animals, but I began to realise that there was some potential for them here and I started a clinic every Tuesday evening, spaying cats and that. I built a little surgery, over there between the trees at the end of the garden, which we thought was adequate for what small animal work there was. But it began to snowball, until we had people standing all the way down to the front gate on a really busy night. Quite a few people afterwards said they used to come just to see the garden in the summer!'

After eight or nine years in the garden surgery Tony and his partner began to develop a new surgery on what is the site of the practice today. It amazes Tony to think that the practice now has a couple of X-ray rooms, two consulting rooms, a proper operating theatre, an animal cage room, good sterilisers, plenty of instruments, and computerised blood-testing machines for immediate results. All this is new since Tony left, apart from the X-ray machine.

Before the practice had its own X-ray machine, Tony remembers a big, fat labrador coming in. It had had a single puppy and it was impossible to feel whether or not there were any more to come. He didn't want to do a caesarean through all that fat if there was nothing in there, so he rang a friend at Scarborough and sent the dog there to be X-rayed. The results were through within the hour, showing that there were no more puppies. He later discovered that Hutton had simply taken the dog across the road to the local hospital for her X-ray.

The practice at Pickering covers a radius of about twenty miles. There are other practices scattered around at Kirby, Malton, Scarborough and so on and he always got on very amicably with them, but for many years there was a strong sense of isolation: 'In those days a lot of my generation worked on their own and had very little contact with the rest of the profession. The *Veterinary Record* came in once a week to keep you up to date, and you depended a lot on what the reps told you about new drugs. You'd spend hours and hours driving round; you'd have a short period of five or ten minutes on a farm, so if you made ten calls in a day you had a hundred minutes of company. For the rest of the day you were absolutely on your own and the isolation was quite difficult. But that is slowly altering now. The practice that I used to run virtually on my own here is now a three-man one and I know for a fact that they don't work half the hours that I used to!'

Tony notices that most of those from veterinary schools today no longer have an agricultural or veterinary background: they have a good academic record instead. 'I remember one particular student who came to see practice here in his fourth year. We were out on a country lane one day waiting for some cattle to be driven in; I was standing in a gap in this wheat field, he was standing in a gap further down, trying to keep the cattle from getting through the hedge. I pulled a head of wheat and rubbed out the grains, blew off the chaff and ate them – I like a bit of green wheat. So he immediately grabbed a head of barley and started rubbing that. "Don't do that," I said, "you'll choke. That's barley." And he said, "How do you know the difference?" A fourth-year student at Edinburgh and he didn't know the difference between barley and wheat!

'Our next call was a farm at Middleton, good practical hard-working lads. I was busy with the sheep and out of the corner of my eye I saw that he'd picked up a mangel wurzel and was looking at it. I finished with the sheep and he said, "By the way, what's this root?" The farmer looked at me and spat! And whispered to me, "I hope you're not going to employ that sort."

'We had taken on our first girl a couple of years earlier and I remember the ones that came for interview: one was a terrible mess and was really only looking for somewhere to live, another looked as if she had stepped straight out of the pages of Vogue, very daintily dressed, beautiful, quite a cracker, who'd been in large animal practice in Wales. A third was a different kettle of fish altogether. She had the usual dirt-stained fingernails that all vets get and she looked like she could work. We took her on, though I was a bit dubious about her facing all these north Yorkshire farmers, who were very conservative. But she proved her worth.

'I remember one very old-fashioned farmer whose son was taking over the farm and a cow wanted cleansing. The son had told his father to watch out for the vet coming. Morag pulled into the yard and began to put on her calving apron. The old man went to his daughter-in-law and said, "Hey, there's a woman come into yard, she's putting the big apron on." "Yes," said his daughter-in-law, "he's asked the vet to come." "Nay," he said, his eyes wide open, "it's a woman – she's never come to cleanse a cow! A *woman*!" And I thought to myself, "She'll soon show you!"

'In my early days in Northumberland and Cumberland and Lincolnshire and here in Pickering, farmers took your visit as an occasion for the exchange of news. Men are good gossipers, you know. The visit of the vet was a family occasion: the farmer's wife set the tea with scones and you had a bit of a chat and they took the long overdue bill from behind the clock and settled it. They'd tell you all sorts of things: matrimonial problems, life problems, their hopes and beliefs, intimate things about their relations, their financial position, legal matters, a million and one things. In many cases you could help; you had read more widely than they had, you came across other people with the same problems. You were a counsellor and a news carrier besides being a visiting vet. It's always a help just to talk to somebody.

'They are isolated, you see; that's why farmers have a higher rate of suicide. That and the pressures. I used to see farmers lose all their herd with TB or brucellosis, having to slaughter the lot. Terrible, after years and years and generations of breeding. No wonder some of them become suicidal. And now it's the same with BSE.'

The isolation probably also perpetuated some of the old beliefs among many of the farmers that Tony visited during the 1950s. 'I can well remember going round trying to persuade some of the more old-fashioned farmers to have their cows tested in the days when it was still optional. There was a farmer in Cumberland, had a beautiful herd of pedigree Shorthorn cows, forty of them in a stone barn, tied up for the winter. I was trying to persuade him to have them tested for brucellosis – that's contagious abortion. "Oh no, no, young man," he said, "won't get brucellosis here, you don't know what you're talking about." And then he explained. "Well," he said, "an aborted foetus is buried under the door step." There was a big stone slab of a step at the end of the cow byre. "And," he said, "you see these little bags of salt?" Well, I hadn't noticed, but each cow had hanging over it a little linen sachet of salt. "Well, you see, young man," he said, "my father always told me, and my grandfather before him, you won't get contagious abortion in the herd if you visit old so-and-so. He's a wise man, he's the seventh son of a seventh son. You go and see him and you take him some silver coin." Half-crowns, I suppose, in those days. And if I remember the story right, this wise man had given the farmer a little pottery figure of a cow and told him to bring a seven-pound bag of salt and for his wife to make these little linen sachets; told him to come back in a week's time, saying he was going to bury the little figurine of a cow in a particular place. So he went back after a week, paid the fee and took all these little bags filled with salt, one to be hung over each cow. "And," the farmer told me, "I've never had a contagious abortion in the herd." And that was true, he never had. All the cows passed the test when it became compulsory.

'Even with veterinary medicines there was a strong belief, verging on black magic really, about the person who dispensed it – he had to have the right authority. Somebody in Northumberland told me, "Don't want you young vets on the place." So I said, "Well, if it's a difficult case Mr Pickering will always back us up." "Oh, it's 'im as well," said the farmer, "I only have 'im because 'is father's dead." The father had still been practising in his eighties, and so was the old vet in Pickering when I was young.

'The other thing was with horses. The old Cleveland Bay is still bred around here – the breed was saved after the war by this woman who had a stud at Danby, she was a client. I went there to a mare that had foaled and retained the afterbirth. Afterwards I thought I'd take away this horrible-looking bloody thing and bury it in the manure heap, so I got the fork out, but she said, "Oh no, no, what are you doing, Tony?" So I told her I was just going to bury it out of sight in the manure heap, where the heat would kill off the bugs. "Oh," she said, "George would be most upset." Well, George was an old fellow in his eighties who still worked on the farm. "Why will George be upset? He isn't here," I said, "it's nine o'clock at night." "Ah," she said, "you see, he believes in the old-fashioned way. He'll hang that cleansing up in the holly bush along the drive. And as long as it's hanging up there, drying in the sun and wind, then the foal will thrive. It dates back to the old days of Saxon horse worship and the belief that any evil spirits around will concentrate on the afterbirth rather than on the foal, you see."

'Who was I to argue? Anyway, when she semi-retired later on, she moved from the farmhouse and built a bungalow in one of the fields, put up a big stable somewhere there on that wild moorland. Well, I saw old George working on the hedgeside one day so I stopped the car, let the window down, and said, "George, where's Ruth Kitchen?" He told me how to reach her new place. "How's she getting on there?" I asked. "Well, all right I suppose," he said, in broadest Yorkshire of course, "but she'll deay neay good goin' oop there. Aye, the fairies won't like it. The fairies have a girt strong hold over that field." And he wasn't laughing about it, either. The field was called Fairy Cross, but I think she must have sorted the fairies out because she did all right there.

'All that sort of belief has gone; it all disappeared with that generation, though there are still a few lingering traces of it. A lot of farmers round here, all over the north country, the older ones just about retired now, they still believe in "worm in tail".

They used to reckon that there was a worm, eating away the cow's strength when it's what we call a downer. A lot of cows, after they've calved, go down with a paralysis: there's a whole host of different causes and a lot of them are very bad cases; they lie there for two weeks, you do your best and then send them off. Old John Atkinson was the first man to call in if there was a downer cow, not the vet. He used to raise the cow's tail and find that little hollow spot which is actually where we do an epidural injection – you get the needle just between the bones in the tail, just at the root of the tail; you can feel the little space between the bones and you can hit the spinal cord there to freeze up the back end for obstetrics. Old Atkinson used to select this spot and make a cut: there's a little white ligament running down there and he used to raise that and push a piece of onion underneath and pack it with salt and bandage it up. Well, I think it was successful in some cases because all the cow needed was a really strong stimulus to make the effort of getting over the birth and the stiff back end if she'd had a rough calving. And salt and onions when you're sitting around wondering what's in there worked in some cases, and gave it credence.

'A lot has changed. I mean, my own father was one of thirteen children and my mother was one of nine or ten, but I have just three sisters. Round here, these little cottages used to be full of children: there were three little stone cottages (knocked down now for a car park), two-up two-down, and someone told me that when my father and he were young they could remember old Bert somebody living there and sixty-one humans lived in those three stone cottages. And old Bert was a big chap, big paunch I remember, big bulky sort of man; he worked on the farm and every Friday night he used to bring out a great big bundle of straw on his back, nice clean straw. He had the two upstairs bedrooms: boys slept on that side, girls on the other, and the straw was cleaned out every Friday night and fresh straw put down. Then they would have feather beds (very common around here – rather like duvets but you used to sleep on them) on top of the straw as a sort of mattress, very warm. I remember a place in Hamilton, up at Manor Farm, and in one of the bedrooms there was a bed that was a wooden frame with holes drilled in the side, pieces of rope threaded across like a shoelace, and a straw-filled mattress on top of that. I've slept on a straw-filled mattress with a feather bed on top. Terribly warm in summer but lovely and cosy in winter.'

Tony recognises what a hard life was lived by many of his older clients, especially those up on the moors. There was one farmer, since retired, on a very hard little moorland farm, who could not read or write and would sign his cheques with two or three crosses. 'He said to me, "You know, I came out of the army and started up here on this bit of moorland, I had one horse and we used to try and plough up some of this rough moorland, to grow a crop in. In springtime I've seen us both so tired that we neither of us could walk home and I used to sleep in the field with the horse." He was a believer in all sorts and he'd try anything on a cow rather than get the vet (he never even earned enough to pay income tax). One of his favourite drenches was a pound of currants mixed with milk, poured down the cow's throat. Search me what it was supposed to do! Laxative, I suppose.

'He used to make besoms out of ling or heather. I asked him once to show me how he did it. "Well," he said, "we'll spend a day cutting ling and a day gathering hazel poles for a shaft in the woods. Then two or three days making besoms." They only had oil lamps in the house, and no radio or television, and he and his wife used to spend their evenings making besoms. They'd bring them down to a dealer in Pickering who collected besoms from several farmers who made them, and they'd be sold to the steelworks at Middlesborough. They used to get 2s 6d a dozen.'

Looking back on his own career, Tony recalls the great variety of animals that he saw in his practice. 'You know those four goats I had when I was nine or ten years old, and all through the war? Just the fact that you were known to have physically kept goats yourself, people thought you were an expert on goats. A lot of goats were kept round here and the goat-keepers would tell all their friends that I was an expert. I'm no more an expert on goats than anybody else but because I had actually kept them it went down big with the goat people.

'There's a zoo here, Flamingo Park Zoo about three miles away. They have all sorts – polar bears, wolves, lions, tigers. We did a few calls there now and then, cattle work and sheep, saw a few camels, but most of all I remember the dolphins. What on earth could I know about dolphins? The dolphin man loaned me this book from America, a great big tome all about the diseases of cetaceans and dolphins, cost him about £60. I remember sitting up until about two in the morning, trying to digest a bit of information out of this book before I went down there. Then I said, "How am I going to examine these things swimming round the pool?" "Oh, that's no problem," he said. He blew a whistle and these two dolphins looked up, came towards us, shot out of the water on to this platform and lay there, laughing at me. "There you are," he said, "you can listen to their hearts." He told them to open their mouths and I could look down their tonsils and look at their teeth – it was absolutely amazing. They had ulcerations on the skin and we came to the conclusion that it was the artificial salinity of the pool water. They were using tap water with salt added and I'm sure that isn't the same as sea water!'

But Tony was more often dealing with cats than with dolphins: 'This little maiden lady, she was crippled almost double with arthritis, her chin nearly touching her knees: she had about six cats and had tremendous faith in me about her cats. One day the fatal day had come for this poor old cat and she wanted it to be put to sleep. There she was, with the cat in the box, and she said to me, "Now, I'm going up into the bedroom out of the way. Everything you need is on the table." There was a pencil, some paper, a plastic bag, a piece of old linen sheet, needle and thread and a ruler. "When you put the cat down," she said, "I want you to measure it with the ruler and write the measurements on the bit of paper so that I can have a box made at the joiners. Then I want you to put it in the plastic bag and then put it on the linen sheet and sew it up like a shroud with the needle and thread. And then I wonder if you'd be so kind as to call at the joiners to ask them to make a little box for me." Poor old thing; she was so crippled with arthritis, so I did all this for her and went round to the joiners. He said he had just the thing: some old army ammunition boxes, quite strongly made and just about the right size. "It's a bit big, really," he said, "but it'll do."

'Next time I went to see the old lady, three months later, she complained bitterly. "That box," she said, "I put the cat in and it was far too big – I couldn't lift it. All I could do was put it under the bed. I wonder if you could get it out for me?" Two or three months and the cat was still there, in the box under the bed! It was pretty well sealed; it was in a plastic bag and it had been lined with white lead paint. Then she said, "I wonder if you'd contact the vicar at Scalby" (that was near Scarborough, her parents had come from there) "and see if I can have the cat buried near my mother's grave." Well! So I rang the vicar and of course he said that they wouldn't allow animal remains to be buried in consecrated ground; but he knew the family and he'd allow the cat to be buried in his churchyard garden, just over the wall.

'Later on the old lady said, "You know, Mr Poole, I'm getting very old and very frail. I don't know what's going to happen to my cats. Now, I've seen my solicitor and I've left arrangements: if anything happens to me I want you to put all these cats down and have them all put in the coffin with me." I said, "I don't think that's possible – I'll certainly attend to your requirements about putting the cats quietly to sleep, they all know me, but as for the rest I don't know whether it would be allowed." I didn't know then, and I don't know now.

'There was one poor girl, Freda, I used to know when we were schoolchildren. Her husband bought her a kitten and it snowballed from there: at one time she had 112 cats. She kept about fifty of them in this very nice little cottage which her parents had left her, and they never went out of the place. She used to work on a farm nearby and she spent every penny, along with a little bit of money from her parents, on those cats. Anyway, by a continual process of sterilising them as best she could afford (I must have done hundreds of pounds of work for her for nothing), we got her down from 112 to about 82, I think. If there's a cat heaven, she'll go to it, I'm sure. If I'd said, "I want you to sit up with this cat and give it drops every ten minutes, day and night," without doubt she would have done it. Her clothing reeked of cats; everybody would leave when she came into the waiting-room and we'd have to get out the aerosol afterwards. She wore an old sheepskin coat that was absolutely saturated in cat. Poor girl. When she died, seventy or eighty cats had to be put down. She had dedicated her life to them.'

Other animals have fared less well, albeit perhaps more through ignorance than deliberate cruelty. 'There was the Reverend Tom Barker, an eccentric, living in this enormous old vicarage with old-fashioned stone flag floors. He lived there with his mother, in her eighties, who always wore a black dress and a little old-fashioned lace cap. He was an odd character. He had a bad back and we'd gone into church one day for a funeral, and found Reverend Barker lying flat out in the aisle trying to ease his back. And he was a bit absent-minded, you see. He got up and said, "Dearly beloved, we are here gathered to celebrate holy matrimony ..." That sort of thing. And he used to ride his bike over to the church without any tyres on it, just rattling along on the iron rims.

'Tom was a great musician and he had a grand piano and stacks of music standing two or three feet high all over the room. And those little cylindrical Aladdin paraffin stoves all over to keep a bit of temperature in the place. They'd be sitting at the breakfast table on which there'd be days and days of dirty cups and teapots and things, and they'd both be working at these books. They were translating medieval Latin poetry into English.

'Now, he had this big Airedale dog that had a whole mass of cancerous growth all around under its tail: the stench was dreadful. I used to go and see this dog, get there about half past nine in the morning, and it wasn't house-trained so there was mess all over the stone floor.

'Anyway, this dog got worse and worse and the stench was dreadful, and this poor old lady in her mid-eighties was scrubbing these stone floors on her hands and knees. So eventually I said, "I'll have to take this dog down to the surgery. I'll give it an anaesthetic and have a proper examination of what is going on." And I was thinking to myself, it's not coming back either. They agreed that I could take it and I dragged the thing into my car, tied his lead to the door handle, opened all the windows because the stench was so overwhelming, got it into the surgery. I had one look at it and it was terrible, poor thing, so I put it down. Shortly afterwards he rang through asking when he could expect to have the dog back. "I'm terribly sorry, Reverend," I said, "but while it was under the anaesthetic I thought it was kinder to let it pass away." That really upset him: "Oh, but you see," he said, "that dog had been sent to us by God to see how much my mother and I could endure. It was a trial sent by God." "Ah," I said, "well, I think God must have taken a hand in this and allowed me to ..." "Well, yes," he said, "it could be, couldn't it?" I don't think he realised how much that poor dog was suffering. I don't think he knew how cruel it was.'

Many of Tony's stories are worthy of James Herriot's books and he agrees. 'I've often said that nothing has ever happened to Herriot that hasn't happened to me!' And this must be true: the real 'Herriot' lived and practised only twenty or thirty miles away from Pickering.

He had made a vow to himself that he would retire when he had done one million miles, and that is exactly what he did. Or, more realistically: 'My partner Peter Fernie died just a few months before his pension and I have seen several die in their early sixties by working so hard, dying in harness. I remember saying to myself that I wasn't going to do the same, so as soon as I was out of debt with buying property and assistants' cars and all that, I backed out – I retired six years ago.'

He now has more time to tend his well stocked garden, in which every plant reminds him of someone or somewhere. He also has a good collection of hostas although they have suffered badly from hungry snails over the years: 'For three years, I went out between midnight and two in the morning with a torch to collect those snails by the bucketful every night. I have a friend who runs a small place looking after wildlife – wild birds, badgers, deer, all sorts – and this year she's had about three dozen fox cubs brought in. And foxes like snails, plenty of calcium for them ...'

It seems such a practical and ecologically sound solution to every gardener's problem, and it is very typical of this quiet and sensible Yorkshireman, Tony Poole.

Black rhino and dancing bears

oooo

Ascott-under-Wychwood is a tiny and typically English stone village, set peacefully amid open fields and approached by quiet lanes that tangle together vaguely by a small green and the old village school. There is a level-crossing here over a single railway track that must surely bear very few trains a day. The village, outwardly, reminds one of the rural villages of the 1940s.

A couple of rucksacked walkers saunter along a long driveway across the fields: this is part of a long-distance Way and hereabouts it passes along the banks of the River Evenlode. At the end of the drive a fine cluster of massive and venerable stone barns forms a spacious farmyard, one side of which is bordered by a superb old manor house that dates back possibly to the eleventh century. Most of the barns now house a family antique furniture restoration venture: bits of furniture, whole or in pieces, are stacked in haylofts and in the passages at the back of the barns where once the cows would have wandered to their milking stations at dawn and at dusk.

There is an old granary on staddle stones and in one of the high barn walls are the unmistakable entrances of a manorial pigeon loft. This steading reeks of history; there is even the mound of an ancient motte-and-bailey castle beside the house. The feeling of a stronghold is reflected in the setting of open fields flanked along one winding boundary by the lazy little river and on another by a distant railway embankment that seems more like an ancient earthwork than a modern one and does not intrude in the least upon the quiet browsing of the sheep. There is a magic about this place.

At the heavy oak door of the manor house, my knocking is greeted by deep, loud barking. Several large black dogs bound out in friendly welcome: they are labrador/wolfhound crosses, of several generations, and a very handsome combination it is – a largely labrador body with a whiskered wolfhound face. Above the barking, the house is filled with the booming sound of Country and Western music. John Gripper emerges, a large man comfortably dressed in old trousers, wearing well worn trainers on his feet, a man wholly at ease with himself who cares not a jot for appearances. His warm and friendly wife Annie is also comfortably and unpretentiously dressed, with her hair drawn back in a fair ponytail. There is something of the 'earth mother' about her and a strong feeling of a couple devoted to their family, and that is borne out in later conversation: the family is very important to them both. They have four children and several grandchildren and the house reflects the family feeling: it is a little chaotic, decidedly informal and very welcoming. The Aga in the kitchen is a natural focus; and under the wall-benches that surround the family table one gradually becomes aware that a dog or two is peacefully asleep.

John's slightly shambolic appearance is deceptive: he is a man with a keen brain and in his 'retirement' is a highly respected consultant on veterinary practice management. But that is only a small part of his new life. He is man of extraordinarily wide interests and a man who is not content to sit back: he *does* something about matters that deeply interest or concern him. It is fascinating to see what strands in his life led him to his current involvement with, for example, rhino in Africa and bears in

Greece and Turkey. He is a passionate and compassionate man.

Like so many veterinary surgeons, John was not born to a rural life. His early life was spent in Croydon, in Surrey, where his father was an electrical engineer with the local authority. The family was a Quaker one and in due course John went to a Quaker school in York. Although he is no longer a practising Quaker, that background clearly had a great influence on him. For example, he has been a vegetarian since he was a little boy, an option that his schools offered (unusual for the time), and this was because he never liked eating meat and he did like animals. He knew right from his childhood that he wanted to be with animals and that he wanted to be a vet: it was something about which he was single-minded.

'After I left school I did my National Service and went into the army, ending up by mistake in the Royal Army Dental Corps as a "DORA" (dental operating room assistant) in Berlin during the blockade. I also had to do emergency work with the medical corps – road accidents, suicides and the like. That was quite an education for someone straight out of boarding school.

'I came back and managed to get into Edinburgh: the Royal Dick. I had already seen practice in Buckingham during the war. Before I went to college I wanted more farm experience so I worked with a cowman on a dairy farm at Wiveliscombe, where we were hand-milking Dexters – you were almost lying down to get underneath those short-legged little things.

'While I was at Edinburgh I saw a lot of practice, but I also earned money doing different jobs such as selling ice-cream in the summer or temporary post-office work before Christmas. My group at Edinburgh was a little different: we were older because of National Service and we'd had a two-year break from education, so we tended to work and play a little harder. But then I met Annie, who was a midwife in Edinburgh, and we quickly decided to get married. That shocked our parents initially: I was a third-year student with no prospects and she was earning well as a sister. We got married in my third year and found ourselves a furnished flat in a tenement. It worked out very well: I could work at nights because I didn't feel obliged to go out boozing!'

He qualified and in due course became a partner in the Chipping Norton practice of Brian and Mary Pike. The practice was mainly farm work; and then after a year or so, the Pikes suddenly fulfilled a long-held ambition: they went off to New Zealand.

'I had only been qualifed for three or four years and there I was, owning a practice already. That's where I gained my business experience and knowledge of running a practice.'

The practice grew over the years; it became a four-man one and they converted some buildings into a veterinary hospital. But John was getting more and more involved in non-veterinary activities. He was already interested in the politics of the BVA and the Royal College and then he decided to stand for Parliament. He remembers an opponent scoffing about this, asking what a mere veterinary surgeon could possibly know about economics. John was infuriated at the assumption that because he was a vet he couldn't do something else, and he was able to show that some vets know about a lot more than castrating cats and calving cows. In the event he did not become an MP.

The pattern of life in the area was changing. In the early days most of the work was with farm livestock, particularly cattle: there were fifty to sixty dairy herds in the practice's area, most of them with only twenty or thirty cows in each herd. 'Each cow had a name, and the farmer would be really worried if an individual cow wasn't eating or was just not quite right. They knew their animals so well. Over the years that changed, and it became 100-cow herds under a farm manager. There were no more of the old early-morning milk-fever cases because they knew how to treat it themselves. And we never got the easy calvings; we were only called out for caesarians and so on. There was much more pregnancy diagnosis and fertility work: you had your hand up a cow's backside all morning. I was much more interested in doing the work I'd first done at the practice, the fire brigade stuff – sick animals, calving, lambing. I was more satisfied by getting an *ill* animal *better*; I was never so interested in the routine fertility work. The whole attitude was changing.

'Another thing changed in this area. It was essentially mixed farming round here but the pressures began to build up on farmers not to keep livestock. There was more money in arable and the hours were more straightforward. We have seen the small family farms break up; we have seen a number of estates taking over the tenant farms, and now they don't even farm them themselves but get other people in to do it. The pattern of farm ownership has changed, and livestock isn't here any more. But there has been a terrific growth in horse work. We also saw that small animal practice was developing, so we encouraged that with our veterinary hospital and we set up three branch surgeries for small animal work.

'The final change for the practice was about fifteen years ago when we were asked by the Cotswold Wildlife Park to take on their zoo work. I really got interested in that. We spent a whole day a week at the zoo, as well as doing any emergency work that occurred. Then when the Zoo Licensing Act came in, I became a zoo inspector.

'There were three white rhino at the wildlife park and I remember the first time I handled rhinos, when we painted insecticide on them because of all the flies around their ears and eyes. But I had no problems, even if it was the first time. I always believe that animals can detect if you are frightened, and I'm not afraid of any animal, even in the bush.

'There were little things like taking out a panther's tooth, dealing with monkeys, mostly run-of-the-mill stuff with only one or two emergencies; but it was all interesting and it attracted exotic work to us from people with wildlife. There was a good snake section at the park, for example, so we started getting people who had pet snakes and so on.'

They were still living next to the surgery in Chipping Norton and decided to move out to Ascott-under-Wychwood. Then he decided to leave the practice, wanting to develop some of his other interests. He was only in his fifties, and the timing was deliberate.

'If you stay in practice too long you are a bit clapped out and probably do nothing more than a little gardening and watching the telly. If you get out at fifty-five, there is much more opportunity to develop new areas. I think it is important that you do different things in life, that you have different challenges. Everything I do now is linked with my veterinary background but there are far more openings for veterinary surgeons than simply veterinary practice. We have all had a university education and we do have more to offer the community as a whole.'

Since selling the partnership eight years ago he has come to divide his time between what he describes as 'charitable' and 'non-charitable' work (that is, work for which he is paid: he specialises in business management, veterinary or otherwise). It is in his charitable work that the warmth and passion of the man really finds its outlet, and he finds that he is increasingly altering the balance of his life away from business and back towards animal welfare. As well as working with the Prince of Wales Trust, helping young business people make a start, he acts as veterinary consultant to two special charities: the Born Free Foundation and the World Society for the Protection of Animals (whose acronym is pronounced 'whisper'). He frequently travels abroad on WSPA's behalf and his tasks include advice on matters such as setting up sanctuaries in Greece and Turkey for captive 'dancing' bears:

'They rescue these dancing bears off the streets and keep them in holding pens while they are building sanctuaries in the mountains of northern Greece and one in Turkey. I have assessed the situation in both countries for them, given them an overview.'

His involvement with WSPA came about by a chance meeting when he was supplying veterinary drugs through his small export company. At the time the association had gone into the Gulf war to help the huge number of oiled birds and the deserted zoo animals in Kuwait. They asked Gripper to visit another war zone: Croatia, where there was considerable concern about the famous stud of Lipizzaner horses and about dogs and farm animals being shot and being killed by landmines. So he went out with the Royal Army Veterinary Corps and visited the front line to find out what was happening to the animals, something which most people had overlooked.

'I had never been in a war situation before; there were shells and sniper fire and refugees everywhere. I came back from that situation very angry indeed with our government's attitude to the war. You see, most wars that you read about are between people who have different religions to ours or different ways of life, but in Croatia the farmers and people we met were living the same sort of life as we did, in normal times, and it really came home to me.

'I was also shocked at what people were actually doing to each other in this war, in its early stages. The atrocities were quite horrific. I had never imagined that anybody could apparently take a delight in doing these horrific things. I was only there a week but I came back completely shocked. I had gone to look at the serious situation for the animals but I came back far more concerned about the whole war and the way it was affecting the people of Croatia.'

He also became involved with animal life in Africa. 'When I left the practice, I was asked to go to Tanzania for the FAO, to do a project looking at veterinary services and privatisation. I was out there for three months and have since been back to various countries – Kenya, Uganda, Nigeria – and I *like* Africa! There was a time when I was tempted to buy a farm in Zimbabwe. But that was when our four parents were alive and we had our close family of four children and there is no way we would have left this country with those family connections. The grandparents are gone now but we have the grandchildren coming on ...'

It was a family connection in Africa that led to another passion about which, typically, he has taken active and practical steps: 'I have a cousin, Ray Gripper, living in Zimbabwe. We went over there for a holiday and went down to the midlands where Bob Swift had a farm. I'd seen some of the rhino poaching and was very concerned about it. I got chatting with Bob, who said that he'd really like to have rhino on the farms, joining with several farmers as a conservancy to protect them, because he wasn't too happy about the national parks. This was about four years ago, when there were about two thousand black rhino. Today there are only about two hundred there.

'I went round Kenya to look at rhino sanctuaries there. We raised money and now we have about forty black rhino on the twenty farms that got together to create a 250,000-acre conservancy with fences, guards, radio telephones, transport and other equipment, a lot of it funded from money raised in the UK. They are succeeding in keeping the poachers away, but there are many political and other problems. We believe, however, that by linking tourism with the black rhino we can bring some money into the country, and save the rhino at the same time.

'There are fewer than 3,000 black rhino worldwide, compared with about 10,000 white rhino. Somebody shipped some out to Dallas and Australia with the idea of captive-breeding, and then returning the progeny to Africa when the wild population becomes extinct, but the species doesn't breed well in captivity. Anyway, I believe very strongly that to keep an animal like that you must keep it in its own habitat and protect it there, rather than put it in a zoo. Many animals can't cope in the wild after captive breeding – a wild-dog pack, for example, couldn't cope in the wild after release because the animals had never been taught by their elders how to catch prey. It's the same with bears: the mother needs to teach them about which berries and so on to feed up on for the winter. And there is also the problem of disease being introduced into the wild if there is something like BSE in zoo animals.'

John Gripper is definitely a man with a mission – or several missions – and he brings a good dose of down-to-earth realism into the arguments about animal welfare that sometimes become more emotional than practical. He *knows* about animals; he has known about them all his life and he has always put that knowledge to practical purpose, especially as a veterinary surgeon dedicated to healing the sick ones. The dancing bears and the black rhino have the right man on their side.

OF FARRIERS AND COW DOCTORS

ooooo

Warwickshire, home of the Royal Agricultural Society of England's permanent showground at Stoneleigh, is an appropriate county for a recent historical exhibition called 'The Making of the Vet'. The exhibition looked at the work of veterinary surgeons, and of the farriers and cow doctors who preceded them, over the last 250 years within the county. Among the many intriguing items on display were a bill sent out in the 1930s by 'Mr Walker, a castrator from Long Compton' and a photograph of 'William Walker, the Cow Doctor of Long Compton, south Warwickshire'. Instruments and reference books used by Walker were also displayed.

William Walker's grandson, Alan Walker, is a veterinary surgeon practising from Hook Norton, just over the border into Oxfordshire on the heavier ironstone soil. The approach to the village is a delight, across fields that seem to grow smaller and smaller, with numerous fruit trees in the hedgerow along the quiet lane. The village itself is hidden until you pass under an archway of trees and suddenly, there it is, all honey-stone cottages, some with thatch and some with stone roofs. It is a most peaceful, pretty village.

The surgery has a splendid yard with loose-boxes and lambing quarters. Within the unpretentious but quite extensive surgery building there is much activity of veterinary nurses and office staff, toing and froing but very relaxed and friendly.

Alan Walker ambles in, a large, affable man with short brown hair. The first impression is of an overgrown schoolboy, looking much younger than his actual age (he was born in 1946). On the move out of doors, however, there is a degree of stiffness to his gait that suggests perhaps a problem with his hips, though he does not admit to it. We climb into his car with its bootful of veterinary bits and pieces, apparently thrown in at random but their whereabouts all known to him. There is a horse-head mascot on the car bonnet: Alan is a horse vet by preference.

On the long drive to a distant client somewhere near Rugby, Alan is constantly pointing out local landmarks and giving little potted local histories, both general and personal. This man knows and loves this area; after all, his family has lived around here for many generations and he can trace his ancestral 'vets' back to the sixteenth century. 'They were farriers, blacksmiths, cattle doctors in those days, always in Long Compton, which was conveniently placed on the old London coaching road about halfway between Oxford and Birmingham. It was where they would have a changeover of the horses, which meant that they needed people to shoe them and deal with any problems they might have. So my forefathers were right there. They were country people, and as well as shoeing horses, they used all sorts of herbal remedies, some of which I still use today.

'Then, when the railways came and coaching went into decline, the railway companies used to bring cattle and sheep, bought cheaply from the Welsh hills, and unload them at Moreton station. They'd be taken by drovers over to Banbury (another big railway centre) to go to the east of the country for good prices. The main drovers' route was through Long Compton, and so my family became cattle doctors as well as farriers.'

In our tour of the countryside between Hook Norton and Rugby he points out the route of the old droveways and the tollgates that the drovers did their best to avoid along the way. At intervals he points out some of the many farms within his practice, too, with comments on the characters and excellence of stockmen and others.

The cattle doctors seemed to spend most of their time dealing with lameness and castrations, and also de-horning the cattle – almost an insult in a region which had once been dominated by the splendid Longhorn breed of the Midlands. They had no medicines other than their own remedies, and they were adept at techniques such as pumping up a milk-fever cow's udder so that the pressure would stop the flow of milk and the loss of calcium that accompanied it.

'My grandfather, William James Walker, continued the tradition; they handed everything down, father to son, and he had learned everything from his own father, also William. He still did his rounds in a pony and trap, dressed in breeches and gaiters and wearing a grey bowler hat. He was known as "Dr" Walker and I still have his horse twitch. Unfortunately he was killed in a car accident, in 1946, at the age of sixty-nine.'

'My father, Joseph John Walker (known as Jack), born in 1911, and his brother Alf were both veterinary practitioners. Before the 1950s anybody could practise in veterinary work, but then they brought in this new regulation: anybody in practice in 1953 but who had not qualified through college was invited to sign a supplementary veterinary register: they had to go to Portman Square and prove that they had earned their living mainly by veterinary means in the seven years since the war. How did they prove it? By the fact that they'd been paid! Farmers are very shrewd judges of people, especially when it involves money. So my father and uncle were both on the supplementary register as veterinary practitioners. The ones before that didn't need to be on any register, as there had been no control.

'The work then was mostly large animals and horses, and a bit with pigs and poultry. They would not have done anything with small animals, apart from perhaps a working sheepdog now and then. Father worked with William right through the war, but when, soon after its end, William died in 1946, he moved from Long Compton – and was denounced for it by the family: his mother thought it a heresy that there were no Walkers in Long Compton any more. Alf was in the yeomanry and as much a farmer as a practitioner, but veterinary work had been father's sole means of living. He moved to Burmington in 1949 and continued the practice there. He was very much a horse man but did cattle and sheep as well, and would look at the old cottage pig or whatever. He did not shoe horses; nor had William, but William's father had done so.

'Father went into partnership at Burmington but it didn't work out very well: he had always been very much his own man. If he didn't like someone, he wouldn't go there. If he started treating something and they didn't have faith in him, he'd not go back again. He and I never hit it off very well until my mother died and I got to know him better for the last ten years of his life. He died at the age of seventy-seven.'

Alan was born in July 1946; his grandfather died five months later, happy to know that Jack had a son to continue the family tradition. In due course Alan went to Cambridge but not to study veterinary medicine: he did a degree in biology and a doctorate in biochemistry first. Naturally he had always been interested in veterinary work, but on leaving school his A-levels had not been good enough to enter veterinary college immediately. Therefore it was not until 1981 that he finally qualified.

'In later years, father had terrible arthritis in his hips and got very bad breath! He'd had many kicks from horses and been knocked around quite a bit. The practice was dwindling; he really wasn't physically capable of handling it alone. But people were loyal to him; I still go to some of his old friends even now. He was hanging on until I'd finished my five-year training, expecting me to join him in the practice. I really didn't want to come straight back home, but he was so immobile that I had to. I agreed, on condition that father worked for me, not the other way round. Then I moved the practice to Hook Norton and started there in September, 1981, living over the surgery and paying an old boy to drive my father if the old chaps wanted to see him.

'Within five years of my father giving up work entirely, I went from being single-handed to three of us. Now we have six vets, four nurses, three receptionists and two secretaries and we have been computerised for the last ten years. It's a mixed practice but there is still a lot of large animal work, perhaps eighty per cent, and the biggest single thing is horses, which I like. I don't do any small animal work myself.'

We arrive at the clients' stables near Rugby, a big old stone farmhouse with a large cobbled yard surrounded by looseboxes, assorted horses peering over every stable door. A plump, friendly yellow labrador accompanies us as Alan makes his rounds, first of all checking over a horse for sale after enquiring, 'Is he a gentleman behind?' He sounds out a snotty-nostrilled mare with a possible heart problem, looking for a murmur and finding her 'thick in her wind'. They lunge the mare in a muddy field, watched by a couple of housecows. In a loosebox, Alan's next task is to rasp the teeth of a very active young stallion, and then those of an older, quieter mare. Another pony has an enormous wart and Alan treats it with his own ointment.

'That sarcoid wart,' he says later, 'I inherited the recipe; it's more than a hundred years old. Father used to make it up himself. They all made up their own stuff, their powders and their drenches and so on, getting the materials from a wholesale chemist. There was a big one in Coventry. I go to Loveridges in Southampton for mine. I use a lot of herbal remedies. I recognise the need for homoeopathy, too; a lot of clients like it although it is quite expensive. I've tried things like snake venom but I don't think it works.

'A lot of the herbs are Indian. I use some on nervous racehorses: I did that with one neurotic horse, lovely remedy for it, and the horse finished second. They were over the moon with it. I use herbal remedies for joint ill. I use hellebore; comfrey for wounds and for encouraging horses to eat; ivy for sheep; arsenic for conditioning horses – it really makes them shine, and all the old carters used it every week. Some of the stuff I can't get any more, or not easily, but firms such as Loveridges or Triple Crown usually help, or I collect herbs from the garden – often the client's garden. The herbs that I do use, I use quite frequently; my father would have used many more.

'As well as herbs and conventional drugs, I also use ultrasound and laser and Faradic machines, electromagnetic pulse machines, and a fibre-optic endoscope.'

He talks of other treatments increasingly used by some vets, including therapeutic swimming. Alan's father used to 'swim' horses years and years ago, well ahead of his time; it was the ideal exercise for a lame horse that could not bear its own weight, or for pulled muscles here and there. He would swim them in the canal, above the loch gates, with a man on a rope on either towpath.

We pass through Shipston and then Burmington; Alan points out the old coaching road and its sturdy, stonebuilt lodges. Finally we come to Long Compton itself. The area hereabouts is one of gentle hills and there is a friendly feel to the landscape. In the village of stone houses we pass an old stone on which the old fellows used to sit and watch the horses go by.

'This is the old road. The sheep came along here with the drovers, but there was a tollgate at the top – so much a head to go through – and so they found ways round. Now we're passing the Rollright Stones and the King Stone.' There are fine views from up here and a strong sense of place. Alan relates the legend of the Stones.

There can be very few rural practices left now that can boast a family connection stretching back over four hundred years. Alan's predecessors – all those cattle doctors, castrators and farriers – would never have dreamed that at Hook Norton there would be a formal 'veterinary hospital' dealing with everything from Shire horses to pet mice, with its own laboratory and its special on-site facilities for diagnosing and treating the ailments of horses, cattle, sheep and goats. Yet despite all the advances in this ultra-modern practice, Alan Walker is very proud to retain the old-fashioned image of being a caring country practice, where animal welfare is of the utmost importance and where, when modern treatments are inadequate, he can fall back on the family herbal remedies that have proved themselves over the centuries.

On the shelf of his office in the surgery, above the computer on the desk, Alan still has countless old books well thumbed by his father, his grandfather and no doubt his great-grandfather as well. Among them is a handwritten notebook, its fly page entitled *The Recept Book for Cattle*. It contains page after page of recipes for cures, everything from coughs and indigestion to scour and strains, warts and wounds. Recipes gleaned from various sources are written on scraps of paper or old post-cards stuffed between the pages, some clearly very old by the style of the writing and the fragility of the paper. It is a veritable treasure-chest, and it is Alan Walker's heritage.

INTEGRATED ALTERNATIVES

ooooo

It is a pleasant and peaceful village, Stanford-in-the-Vale; you can walk its lanes at dusk and meet not a soul. We go down a footpath off the lane and cross a makeshift footbridge into a miniature wilderness of brambles, nettles and hawthorn bushes, finding our way along a muddy track made by a wandering pony and donkey: we have come to take a look at the pony. In the twilight we can see, sheltered in a grazing glade at the heart of the wilderness, a small, neatly railed yard and tidily homemade wooden stable. They have been waiting for us: a couple and their children, who had begun to grow restless until the foxes emerged to divert them. This is also an informal wildlife sanctuary.

Christopher Day is greeted warmly and with relief. The children bring the pony out of the stable and it comes with them slowly, lame in the near hind leg. Its companionable donkey follows to keep an eye on everything. Quietly and smoothly, Christopher places his hands on the pony's spine, feeling along its length and finding an immediate reaction from pressure at one point. He inspects the afflicted foot and advises a bread poultice to draw the poisons from it. The pony is noticeably more relaxed.

We return, Chris's little terrier impatient ahead of us, to the big old house in the village that has been Chris's home for all his life: he was born here in January, 1947. There is a big family kitchen with an Aga and an old pine kitchen table that have clearly been a part of the room for a long time: they belong comfortably here. This has been home for a working country family for many years.

In the yard behind the house there is a well built detached surgery, smelling deliciously of herbs and gentle spices, in complete contrast to the normal harsh chemical smells of conventional veterinary surgeries. The lighting is pleasant and welcoming, and the room exudes relaxation. Its effects are apparent in a cat that, even at this late hour, is waiting for attention with its owner. The cat is perfectly content and has no fear of this place. And that is one of the secrets of alternative veterinary medicine.

The son of two practising veterinary surgeons, it is hardly surprising that Christopher wanted to be a vet from the age of five. He was passionate about animals: he always preferred, for example, to sleep with the family dog under the table rather than upstairs in his own bed. He is a natural with animals and has retained a boyish enthusiasm for life in general that will always make him look far younger than his years. That is a trait inherited from his father, who has always been young in Christopher's mind. Like his father, the son has 'a habit of enjoying life'.

He speaks very fast indeed, the ideas tumbling over each other; he is full of nervous energy and passion, with a fire in his eyes and a big, warm grin that is probably the first thing people notice about him. His wife, Sheila, is as open-natured and as passionate as he, but is also his sheet-anchor, with a knack of bringing him down to earth when he flies too high.

After 'actively enjoying' school, Christopher went up to Cambridge. Here he kept a candle burning for homoeopathy, 'knowing as a scientist that it could not work but enjoying the challenge of that fact'. He had been about twelve years old when his mother first became interested in homoeopathy for animals, and Christopher had always 'enjoyed the buzz' that it might not work when she experimented with it on some of her cases. This almost perverse delight in challenging the logic of it and then proving in practice that it *can* work is typical of Christopher Day.

After qualifying, he went to a Lancashire practice in Burnley for a year; then he came home to Stanford, to a practice where 'you had to hit the ground running or you were left behind'. His parents were innovative: on the one side his mother was complementing her conventional veterinary work with homoeopathy; and on the other his father was involved, with Chris's support, in preventive work, fertility and animal nutrition, and so successfully that it had reached a point where Chris felt it would be difficult to make more improvements. He had designed a computer program on the nutrition side and was being asked to give lectures on the subject to feed merchants.

He dealt almost entirely with livestock and horses, and became deeply involved in intensive farming. This background would stand in him in good stead when he began experimenting with homoeopathy on a herd basis: farmers would take him seriously. It seemed the next logical step when meeting problems that they could not beat conventionally. He was a good scientist and knew that he needed to prove that the techniques worked.

'The first really objective study I did was with pigs in 1983. We were facing stillbirth problems at a very high rate of 20 per cent, and nobody seemed to be able to solve them. So I said to the old farmer, a bit tongue in cheek, "Shall we try homoeopathy?" He said he'd try anything once. We did a controlled trial with pills for every other sow, and the result was a stillbirth rate of 21per cent in the untreated herd and 10.6 per cent in the treated sows. "Bugger your trial," said the farmer, "put the whole herd on." The following year we did a mastitis trial, with really astounding results. That put homoeopathy on the farm map.'

The homoeopathy began to take over his life: he was not only setting up veterinary courses in London but also visiting Denmark, Norway, Sweden and the United States. In 1987 they held the first international homoeopathy congress in Oxford and it all continued apace. In due course Christopher gave up conventional veterinary work and concentrated wholly on alternative treatments.

'There simply wasn't the time for both. But I could not work in veterinary practice now, and I am very glad that I am out of it. We do acupuncture, laser, homoeopathy, herbal remedies. I'm particularly excited about holistic medicine, especially for horses. If a horse is lame in the fetlock you could give him homoeopathy pills for that, but you would do far better to study his teeth, his lifestyle, his nutrition, the way his saddle fits and everything else about him first. What we are doing now is *integrated* medicine, not homoeopathy.'

This is, of course, a time-consuming approach: Chris reckons to spend an hour with an animal just to find out all about it. He is defensive about terminology: there has been a trend towards calling non-conventional treatments 'complementary' but he disagrees strongly with this. 'It is *alternative* medicine. You could say, if you want, that drug medicine is complementary to alternative medicine!'

He admits to being very lucky with his clients, who seem to love their animals above all. 'There was a woman with a dressage horse; it had given her some wonderful years but she wanted to retire it because it was in too much pain. She had heard about homoeopathy and called us in. I said I would needle it. Well, she said that a vet had stuck a needle in his backside last time and that he would go crazy. So I was shut in the box with the horse, and the animal itself showed me where to put the needle, with his nose. As it happened it was about half an inch from the previous one. It only needed one treatment and then it went back to dressage for another two years.'

From anybody else, this story of equine communication might seem starry eyed and evidence of an excess of missionary zeal. From Christopher, it sounds matter-of-fact and thoroughly reasonable.

There was a shiny black stallion in Wales, diagnosed by its local vet as having laminitis. Conventional treatments were not working: it was being given three injections a day for a week and remained in agony. Christopher went and had a look. 'Belladonna leaped out of the box at you,' he says. 'Nostrils wide and bright red, couldn't put its foot down, eyes wide. Belladonna was the picture; I injected into the vein and within *moments* it was different. Within ten minutes it was walking round its box. Within six weeks it was back serving again.

'We gave instructions for a choice of herbs to continue the treatment and it was fascinating: the horse would devour a certain herb for three days, then refuse that one and devour the other ones instead. It knew what it needed.'

A problem for those who use alternative approaches to veterinary medicine is that they are often the last resort: owners come to them when they have tried every possible conventional treatment, by which stage the animal is often severely ill. 'There was this King Charles spaniel, very, very poorly when he was brought to us. His own vet wanted to put him down: he had lost all his hair and was just one huge scab from top to bottom. He couldn't even recognise his owners and when he came here he hardly moved the first week, eyes all clouded over, peeing like custard. But after a week he started feeling fine. It took about a year, but now he is a divine little dog, looks lovely, eyes crystal clear and a coat like a King Charles rather than a Mexican Hairless.'

Some of Chris's alternative treatments are liberally dosed with common sense. He tells the story of Cleo the python: 'The husband was a bird-watching twitcher and he'd gone away for a few days after some rare bird or other. His wife was left at home to look after Cleo but she knew nothing about snakes, didn't understand them at all. The snake was coughing up blood. It was a weekend and she rang the Cotswold Wildlife Park for help but there were no vets on duty. No local practice would see the snake and eventually she was referred to me. She brought Cleo in a pillow case and dumped it on the table. I asked her what temperature she was keeping Cleo in, but she didn't really know, she thought it was something or other, which sounded a bit low to me.

'We took Cleo out of the pillow case and I noticed a large bulge in her middle. It was a rabbit: she had eaten it a week ago. It turned out that she had flicked the thermostat with her tail so that the ambient temperature had been too low for her to digest this thing. She had a rotten rabbit in there. The homoeopathic picture was high phos. and low pyrogen (phos. is a long and slender type with quick reactions); she was bleeding from the orifices and probably had pneumonia. So I took out my syringe and wondered where to inject – there's plenty of area to choose from with a snake. Anyway, I jabbed it into this pathetic, torpid, almost moribund animal, and quick as a flash, she'd wrapped herself around me and bound me to the leg of the table!

'We gradually persuaded her back into the pillow case. That was Saturday. On Sunday she was fine, and on Monday the woman went to the Wildlife Park for antibiotics. Don't think her husband was ever told what had happened.'

It is getting late now but Chris and Sheila are on the subject of animal experiments, which they both abhor and about which they both became very heated. They have seen too much and they are deeply cynical about many aspects of the chemical industry. 'You know, I wanted to be a vet all my life. I wanted to be as good a vet as I could be. But at college I could see the pit-falls. Now, at the age of forty-seven, having trodden the furrow, I'm rebelling. And I am very glad that I'm swimming in the opposite direction!'

A REAL FAMILY AFFAIR

ooooo

The village of Guiting Power is special. It is tucked away in the Cotswolds, approached by very narrow and lengthy lanes with little in the way of signposts – not the sort of place that you would pass through, but one to which you would only go with intention. It is a delightful stone village, quiet and pleasant, with its church and two small village greens, one with a war memorial and another with a huge chestnut tree. It has the look of an old estate village but is not truly one.

The Days moved to their low but spacious stone house in Guiting Power in 1978 from their family home and practice in Stanford-in-the-Vale. They continued to worked in the Stanford practice on a part-time basis, until Evelyn retired in 1988 because of the effects of spinal and neck arthritis – an occupational hazard. Kenneth retired two years later after a triple bypass heart operation. These two constantly active people, always accustomed to being busy, are now in their seventies. They had been in practice together for most of their married life and it was obviously a good partnership, both professionally and personally. They celebrated their golden wedding anniversary in February, 1994.

Kenneth's childhood was in suburban London. 'I used to disappear on my bike and go to work at stables in Blackheath and Bexley Heath and Shooters Hill. I would do anything for money then! They used to have a clearing house for these hacks, bring them in from fairs, all rogues and bandits. They'd put me on the backs of these ponies to see what the animals would do. The ponies would try to bite your leg and kick you as you got on, then they'd buck and roll with you. And what I learned from that was never to be afraid to admit that you've fallen off! I was absolutely potty about horses. And I did a lot on farms as a boy in the school holidays, learned to milk cows and so on.'

At the age of eleven he decided that he was going to be a vet. Why? 'Well, we had lots of animals when I was a child, birds and rats and rabbits. I bred budgies, and did experiments with colours and so on. I was fascinated with animals. And living in suburbia, I was quite determined that I wanted an outdoor life, a country life, which meant forestry, farming, vetting, something like that. Vetting was my first choice.'

He entered the Royal Veterinary College in London in September, 1938, and it was at college that he met Evelyn. She, too, had had a 'total fascination' with animals all her life and she, too, had decided to be a vet when she was eleven years old.

'We had dogs and cats at home, and I was just so *interested* in them. It was not so much a conscious love of animals as an interest in them. When I decided to be a vet, everyone thought me quite mad. Every year at my school, each new form mistress tried to persuade me not to do this. But I was determined ...'

Evelyn went straight into the second year in January 1940, as the autumn term was fully taken up by the evacuation of the college after the outbreak of World War II. 'Because of the war, in the first year students were evacuated to Reading University; the second year was partly in Reading and partly at Sonning, the third was all at Sonning, and the fourth and fifth years were at Goring, or rather Streatly.'

They variously saw practice while they were at college. 'Of

course,' says Evelyn, 'we saw practice in wartime, when the push was for food production. We were a reserved occupation and were told that we were needed and should not go into the forces or any other war work: our whole motivation was to help the farmers achieve maximum production. That was when these great disease control and eradication schemes got going, because they were vital. In our own lifetime, TB, swine fever and brucellosis have been eradicated. It was quite a challenge.

'Under the old scheme we went round every three months "udder-punching", early in the morning immediately after milking. We'd visit four or five herds, leaving home at 5.30 in the morning. We'd feel each udder, take samples if we were suspicious. TB produced hard, non-painful udders with thin, clear, watery discharge. There could be pulmonary TB cases as well – we would hear their coughing. We had to take sputum samples from the backs of their throats while they coughed in our faces.'

'It was essentially large animal work, with farm animals and horses,' says Kenneth, 'with just a little small animal work for the gentry and also for farm workers, but we didn't charge the latter much, if anything at all. Evelyn would do her small animal work in the evenings. I used to calve a cow for a pound, and if it was difficult I'd charge a guinea. They were still blowing up udders in cases of milk fever then: people used to think milk fever was a form of mastitis and so they pumped the udder with acriflavine – and, yes, it did cure some of them. Then in the days shortly before we qualified, there was a Danish vet who had no acriflavine when he was asked to treat a milk fever case. The cow was in extremis, so he just pumped air into the udder anyway and found that this worked just as well, because what actually happened was that the back-pressure halted milk secretion and the drain on blood calcium which occurs very markedly after parturition. The farmers had a lot of faith in the blowing up of udders. When we first went into practice and used calcium solutions injected into the veins for treatment, they always wanted us to pump up the udders as well.'

Kenneth had planned to go to South America in a cattle boat after leaving college but it didn't turn out that way at all: it was straight into work, and straight into the Faringdon practice in which he would spend the rest of his career. He had been asked to join the laconic Irish horse vet, Mr T.A.R. Filgate, at Faringdon when he was still a student seeing practice there, and he was only twenty-seven when Filgate moved to Ireland and the Days took over the entire practice, though they had no money. 'We always say he asked me because I was the only one who cleaned up the kennels properly!'

They had moved into the large stone house in Stanford-in-the-Vale in 1946. It was very much a family home and one for animal lovers; the household and paddock, over the years, would contain about five dogs, assorted goats, sheep, horses and two or three Jersey housecows. 'We had moved into what was one of the densest cattle areas in the country at the time,' Evelyn remarks. By contrast, she had previously spent six months in a Wimbledon practice with Colonel Perry and Charles Perry.

'I clocked eighty hours a week working in the Wimbledon practice. They decided to let me have Charles's Austin 16, but the Perrys were both about 6ft 4in tall and they'd had the seat pushed back for such a long time that it wouldn't fasten forward – it just slid about all over the place. So I went down Wimbledon hill with my bosom in the steering wheel and up the hill clinging on for dear life because the seat kept sliding backwards.

'When I was seeing practice, I learnt to drive in the middle of Leicester in the days when they were using horsedrawn drays amongst the trams. Most of the short-haul work was being done by horses, right through the war, and there were some terrible accidental injuries to them: when those ash shafts broke, they were as sharp as spears.'

'Working horses seemed to lose their importance and their relevance when the war came,' says Kenneth. 'We were moving into mechanical transport.'

Evelyn continues her narrative. 'The Wimbledon practice gave me four guineas a week and my room in Wimbledon, and I put some money aside so that I had money to spend when we got married. Kenneth was in the countryside at the time and kept sending me presents of eggs and honey.

'When I was seeing practice as a student in Derbyshire, during the war, farmers would say to the vet, 'Would you like a drop of milk, or an egg?' And they would not expect him to pay – unless they were big farmers!'

Kenneth, meanwhile, was finding life was fun, which was as it always had been and always would be for him. He has a great capacity for enjoying life, getting the most out of it, and being grateful for it.

'One of the things I found when I was seeing practice as a student, and later in practice as a veterinary surgeon, was that it was the most enormous privilege to be accepted and welcomed in everybody's house in a completely classless fashion. Remember that the country at that stage was still very much in layers: the gentry, the owner-farmers, the tenant farmers, the workers and so on, all very separate. But I was acceptable to all of them. It was such a privilege that they all treated me as an equal, whoever they were.'

They talk about matters of principle and integrity, and the importance of always honouring the trust of their clients: 'I was at Faringdon for such a long time,' says Kenneth, 'that in the end I was vet to some of my original clients' grandsons. And although we had very few social friends, because we were working all the time, all our clients were our friends. I could always pop into a farm to make a phone call and have a cup of tea. I absolutely loved the old farm kitchen with the bacon hanging in the smoke, the big kitchen table covered with everything so that it all had to be pushed aside for you to sit. It was the *welcome* that was so wonderful; they didn't worry about the house being tidy, and if you were dirty from your work it didn't matter. We were in our practice there for a very long time, and so we were trusted. There were never any arguments about our bills ...'

'We never ran up bills that they would not accept ...'

'Always did things as cheaply as I could ...'

Evelyn takes up that point: 'We had a very poor old lady with a cat. We had sulphur drugs and antibiotics but the cat had a virus and we were only treating secondaries. This enthusiastic young assistant produced the latest high-falutin' drug. I said, "What are you going to charge for it?" He said, "Well, there's my time and the medicine and ..." "Do you know," I said, "how much money that old lady hasn't got? You could have used this, which costs far less, with equally good results." It's so important that newly qualified vets should have some idea of the cost of drugs. Even now, when average earnings are so much higher for everybody, it is quite possible to incur too much expense for owners and to cause them terrible anxiety.

'Present-day methods and equipment are marvellously improved but we should also remember what nature herself will do. A golden retriever came in with a broken hind leg, a bad spiral fracture. I took a series of X-rays and said to the owner that the dog could go away for an extremely expensive operation or it could be confined in a large barrel to heal itself, with proper attention to pain control and nursing. I wanted her back at six weeks and six months to take X-ray pictures so that I could show the evidence to students and assistants who had never had spontaneous healing described to them. The leg would be a little short but it would probably be as good a job as internal fixation, because of the nature of the fracture.

'I once took a student with me to visit an alsatian belonging to a groom who had three or four children and was not a well paid man. The dog was very dodgy, very nervous, and it had a broken leg. I asked my companion what we should do about it. He said that it would have to go away and have its leg pinned, and then be in a veterinary hospital for two or three weeks. And I asked what the dog would be like when it came back to a home with small children in it, and how much all this would cost. He didn't know. So I said, "Right, I shall give the dog something now to ease the pain. We'll put a mattress on the floor in the corner there and put a fence across so that it can't run all over the house and to keep the children out of that corner; we'll see that it has food and water there and is properly looked after, and we'll come back in 48 hours." We did so, and the dog was out of immediate pain; its leg swung about if it walked but without hurting. I said we would come back again in another six weeks. That was all we needed to do and it cost very little. The lad said he never knew that such a healing would happen; they'd never taught him that. He was of the generation who would only use supertechnology, because it's there and because that's what he had been taught.'

By now the mother of two small children, Evelyn was doing three hours a morning for the practice, and loved it. 'Mind you, it was all jolly hard work. The cows in the early years still had horns and were as wild as anything – the sucklers and heifers were not used to being handled and people were frightened of them when they came in, so they would be very rough with them. I've been gored and kicked at the same time by cattle. We didn't use crushes then; the cows were tied up but they could still swing their heads and kick. You'd have youngstock in a loosebox and you had to mix in with them. Some of those heifers had never been handled before, and they might be up to three years old in those days. I went into a box to test some heifers one day and had to earmark them – give them a tattoo in the ear with those big calipers, and sometimes I had to put in more than one mark. They got very cross! One of them landed on my knee and kicked it right through. Everybody heard it go crack. And I've been heaved up into a hayrack when marking an ear: a very big man had been holding the cow and we both ended up in the hayrack.'

Evelyn seems to relish her large animal surgery, and remembers a particularly challenging case: 'There was this farmer, could be quite a demanding man, with a good herd of Friesians, some of them very heavy milkers. This was the time when all dairy cows had horns and bullied each other, and one of his most precious ones had her hip knocked down when she was struggling through a doorway. This was an all too common injury: it meant that a corner of the ileum (the large and prominent hip bone) was broken off and the attached muscles would pull it down towards the stifle as the cow walked. In many cases the fractured edge would ride up and down on the shaft of the bone and there would be necrosis and pus formation. The pus would discharge to the outside and attract flies in summer. I saw this cow in spring and was asked what I could do, or she would have to be put down.'

She had no idea, but the farmer asked her to go ahead anyway and, relying on her own ingenuity, she scrubbed up and took her scalpel in hand, working almost blind to dissect out the large piece of bone.

'Mr E. was most encouraging. "You go on, Mrs Day," he kept

saying, "you're doing fine." It was a case of trying to observe first principles, and keeping going. And then I heard an awful thrr thrr thrr: I had hit an artery, and it was pumping, it was a big one. I quickly put on some artery forceps, deep in this cavity. I had also snicked a bit of the oblique tendon, so I had to tie off the artery and repair the tendon. When we got the bone out, the muscle all retracted and left a hole as big as your head. What on earth do I do with this, I wondered. I pulled the skin across to help it to heal, I packed it with a good sulphonamide and left the artery forceps in place for six days. And the whole thing healed up a treat: she just had a little three-corner scar.'

Kenneth points out how different the training had been in their day.

'We were of the early five-year course and had a reasonable scientific education at college; but the point is that we had no rules that were specific – we had no real specific cures for anything. The only specific before penicillin was in general use (and sulphonamides were still extremely expensive) were sodium iodide for wooden tongue and calcium for milk fever. Basically you were treating symptoms and nursing the animals and relying on nature to cure the condition while you kept the animal alive and as comfortable as possible. There was no question of giving it a shot of penicillin. You would sit up all night with a case of mastitis, stripping out the udder, and you'd put mustard plasters on chests in the case of pneumonia. It was the *nursing* that was so important. Your role was to keep the animal alive so that nature could cure it.'

This theme leads neatly into the subject of homoeopathy, which seems to run in the family. Kenneth uses it, but 'I don't like being restricted in any way! I just use it when it seems to be the most appropriate approach in a particular case.'

Evelyn is much more positive about it. 'An older generation

like ours feels more at home with homoeopathy perhaps than the present generation because we all started with the old pharmacopia; we knew more about plants and chemicals and poisons and their actions and uses. The modern vet knows little about those. You have to study your *remedies* and gradually, over many years, you begin to see the picture of each remedy and recognise the picture in the symptoms that you encounter. You learn from your *cases*; you don't start off by saying, "This is penicillin, which treats gram-positive bacteria." It's the other way round. Each remedy is linked with a complete picture of symptoms, not just one symptom or one disease.'

The Days have worked extremely hard all their lives, and even after retirement from practice they continue to work hard and be busy – the secret recipe for not getting old. They describe themselves unfairly as 'garrulous old fools'; but one thing is for sure: they do not need an oxometer. A what? Their son Christopher had told me to be sure to ask his father what an oxometer was.

'He did, did he! Well, easy really. An oxometer is an instrument for measuring bull ...'

And no one could accuse this very honest couple of talking that!